Opposite the Infirmary

A History of the Thackray Company
1902-1990

Penny Wainwright

MEDICAL
MUSEUM
publishing

1997

i

ISBN 1 897849 01 X

CONTENTS

LIST OF PLATES

ACKNOWLEDGEMENTS

Much of the history of Thackray's was to be found in people's memories rather than on library shelves and I am indebted to all those who willingly submitted themselves to interview. Valuable information was provided by members of the Thackray, Wainwright and Gray families, in particular John and Christin Thackray, Freda Davy, my father-in-law Richard Wainwright and Bob Gray; and, above all, Paul Thackray, whose idea the book was in the first place.

The story would not have been complete without first-hand accounts from Thackray's staff; my thanks go especially to Jim Boyd, Frank Dunderdale, Jim Lockhart, Philip Myers, and the late Bill and Peggy Piggin, Jack Ridsdale, Ronnie and Elsie Sowden and Herbert Winters for their lively reminiscences.

Special thanks are due, too, to Alan Humphries, Librarian of the Thackray Medical Museum, whose computer know-how rescued the entire text from oblivion and who guided the transition from manuscript to page proof so skilfully.

Finally, I would like to thank my husband, Martin, for his unfailing encouragement while the book was in preparation.

Introduction

When Charles Frederick Thackray and his friend Henry Scurrah Wainwright bought a Leeds retail pharmacy as a going concern in 1902, they could hardly have foreseen that their business would one day expand to employ more than 700 people, with markets all over the world. In less than a century, the shop was to grow into one of Britain's principal medical companies, manufacturing drugs and instruments, and pioneering the hip replacement operation which has changed the lives of thousands of people.

Could the friends - Thackray newly qualified as a pharmaceutical chemist, Wainwright a young chartered accountant - have dreamt that their £900 investment would go so far? Perhaps. They were eager and enterprising, and looking for a commercial opportunity when Samuel Taylor, "family and dispensing chemist and druggist", offered his business for sale opposite the Leeds General Infirmary in Great George Street.

The shop was renowned as a high-class pharmacy and continued to attract plenty of customers when Thackray and Wainwright took it over. But it was their decision in the early years of the business to move the emphasis from retail to wholesale pharmaceuticals that set the firm on the road to the sort of expansion that the shop could never have achieved on its own.

In the early years, the site of the shop was crucial. Directly opposite the Infirmary, Thackray was well placed to undertake surgical instrument repairs. From a small workshop in a converted stable at the back of the shop, this side of the business grew rapidly. By the First World War, Leeds was becoming a renowned centre of surgery, the home of outstanding surgeons such as Berkeley Moynihan (later Lord Moynihan). The Infirmary came to play an ever increasing role in developing the instrument repair and manufacturing side of the business.

Between the wars, the emphasis of Thackray's activities shifted once more, away from the wholesale pharmaceuticals and dressings that had dominated business during the First

1

War, towards surgical supply. This meant that instrument manufacture increased, and the firm broke new ground by making their own hospital equipment, such as sterilizers and theatre furniture. An exceptional sales team - Chas F., as he came to be known, would take on only qualified pharmacists as representatives - won important distributorships for the company and ensured a healthy export trade.

The creation of a National Health Service in 1948 had a profound effect on the medical supply trade. The massive re-equipping of hospitals involved was good for all sections of Thackray's and provided a sound financial base on which the company could build in the second half of the century.

High quality was the key to their reputation and it was to Thackray's that Sir John Charnley turned to help him develop the replacement hip operation he made his life's work. This remarkable association, not without its stormy passages, was to take the company to the forefront of the orthopaedic world.

The international Thackray company of today, now known by its new name of DePuy, was steered successfully through a constantly changing course by three generations of the families involved. They succeeded in developing a local shop to a provincial business, expanding to a national one, and finally becoming a global company. None of this could have been accomplished without a loyal and dedicated workforce, of whom many stayed more than 25 years with the firm, and others achieved 40 and even 50 years' service.

The firm had its origins, then, in a lock-up shop. And this is where the story begins - with Charles Thackray's predecessor who, coming to Leeds as a young man in the 1860s, took over one of hundreds of premises that had sprung up in the city during Queen Victoria's reign. It was a time of unprecedented expansion and enterprise all over the country; nowhere was this more apparent than in Leeds where, incidentally, Mr Michael Marks - who teamed up with Mr Thomas Spencer - turned his "Penny Bazaar" in Kirkgate Market to good account.

CHAPTER 1

Samuel Taylor's Leeds

Samuel Taylor was probably on the point of retirement when Charles Thackray and Scurrah Wainwright bought his pharmacy, as he had started the business as a young man forty years earlier, in 1862. Taylor came from York and, although watertight evidence about his origins is hard to find, it is likely that the fourteen-year-old Samuel Taylor listed as son of a York Union Bank manager in the 1851 Census is Thackray's predecessor.

As a schoolboy, Samuel Taylor lived with his parents, sister and three brothers at 1 Parliament Street in York. His eldest brother, John, aged twenty-one, is described as a farmer's pupil, Edward, twenty, an architect's clerk, Francis, eighteen, a leather tanner's apprentice and Mary, his sixteen-year-old sister, a scholar. By the time of the next Census, in 1861, Mary and Francis are still living at home, but Samuel, now twenty-four, has left, presumably to go to Leeds.

At the time Taylor arrived in the city, it was suffering the results of huge and rapid expansion caused by the Industrial Revolution. A population of 53,000 citizens in 1801 had quadrupled to just over 200,000 (and by the turn of the century had massively expanded again to 428,000) but housing and amenities had not kept pace with the population growth.

Slums were everywhere: families were crowded together in appalling conditions with little or no sanitation, untreated sewage being tipped into drains and cartloads of dung removed from yards. Such squalor inevitably led to disease, with typhoid and dysentery common killers.

The health of the city's population gave cause for concern, as this extract from the annual report of the House of Recovery for 1865 shows:

"An unusually warm autumn following a wet August seems to have been one of the causes of a virulent outbreak of fever, the character of which was determined by the state of the lower class of dwellings in the town. The evil consequences of shameful overcrowding have become more than usually apparent in that form of epidemic, namely Typhus Fever, which is well known to owe its malignancy to that condition of things. By this unhappy neglect, the ground has been slowly preparing for a fearful harvest of disease ... the epidemic of Small Pox, which raged among us so severely during many months, and which had barely subsided when the present epidemic set in."

Children worked long hours in factories, with little time or energy left for leisure. Dickens's description of Leeds in 1847 as "the beastliest place, one of the nastiest I know" was amply justified. And more than thirty years later George Eliot refers to "the horrible smoke of ugly Leeds".

The city at that time was not culturally developed either. It did have a Philosophical and Literary Society, but no municipal museum existed until 1921, when the Corporation bought the contents of the museum founded by the Society. A triennial music festival was started in 1858, to coincide with the opening, by Queen Victoria, of the Town Hall that year. But the festival lapsed and did not achieve an international reputation until the turn of the century.

Leeds citizens had a say in their own government with the Reform Bill of 1832 which gave them their first Members of Parliament. The relatively small proportion of the population entitled to vote - there was no universal franchise in those days - put pressure on their MPs to condemn child labour. By 1847 the Ten Hours Act, limiting a child's working day, became law, but it was not until 1870 that children were obliged to attend school, too.

For a man born in York like Samuel Taylor, Leeds, with its grim reputation, might have seemed a surprising choice, but against the background of smoke and grime was the spirit of enterprise and opportunity. Expanding railway and canal systems improved communications dramatically: in 1834 the Leeds/Selby line had opened, and by the mid 1800s lines to Bradford, Dewsbury, Thirsk and Manchester were operational; the Aire and Calder Navigation linked the city to Goole Docks and the Humber Estuary, and the Leeds and Liverpool Canal brought the Lancashire ports and cities within easy reach. It was a boom time for industry and Leeds generated much of the production.

Taylor was accustomed to city life, having spent three years gaining experience at Allen & Hanbury's prestigious pharmacy in the City of London, a fact he was proud to state on the handbill announcing the opening of his business in Leeds in 1862. He took over the shop from a fruit and game dealer in the thriving shopping parade of Great George Street; other tradesmen included a shoemaker, ironmonger, cabinet maker, clock and watchmaker, butcher and confectioner, all of whom derived customers from the many big houses then in the area.

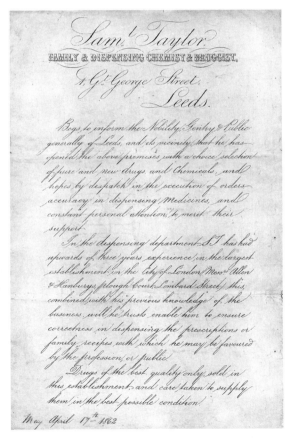

1. Samuel Taylor, having acquired premises in Great George Street from a fruit and game dealer, announced the opening of his pharmacy with this printed handbill. Allen & Hanbury's, with whom he had "studied for upwards of three years", was a prestigious and well known London firm.

Business prospered. Taylor married and, while still at Great George Street, had the first three (two daughters and a son) of their seven children. Also living with the family were two servants and Taylor's assistant, William Knowles. By 1873 he had moved his growing family to Holly Bank, Back Lane, in Chapel Allerton, a pleasant area a couple of miles to the north of the shop, where four more children were born, a boy and three more girls.

Another house move followed in 1886 to nearby 73 Sholebroke Avenue, a street of substantial newly-built houses off Chapeltown Road; by 1894 the family had moved again, to a house named The Mount, in the pretty village of East Keswick, a few miles to the north of Leeds. It seems unlikely that Taylor would have undertaken the eight-mile journey by horse-drawn transport every day. More likely, he would have caught the train from nearby Bardsey station, thereby becoming one of Leeds' early commuters who took advantage of the new Leeds to Wetherby line, completed about fifteen years before.

Taylor's homes in the pleasant residential areas of Chapel Allerton and East Keswick would have been considered good addresses in those days, reflecting his prosperity as the business thrived. In 1881, he acquired 113 Burley Road, and had also become an agent for W.A. Gilbey, wine and spirit merchants. In an 1882-3 trade directory, Taylor was listed as having a warehouse at 24 Portland Street, just around the corner from the shop, but after 1886 the Burley Road and Portland Street premises are not mentioned, and Taylor was recorded at 70 Great George Street only.

Samuel Taylor had opened his business at no.1 Great George Street. Subsequent renumbering as the street developed led to the shop's becoming no.70, although the premises remained the same, at the apex formed by the junction of Portland Street with Great George Street. Further renumbering in 1912 changed the shop's address yet again under Charles Thackray's ownership and it became no. 52. Thus the premises were known by three different addresses during the years it spanned as a pharmacy.

Today, Samuel Taylor would be seen as a respected member of the Leeds business community; he was president of the local Chemists' Association for two years and is recorded as having given 10s 6d to the Leeds Social Improvement Society (President, the Mayor); by 1888 he employed three assistants and was

6

entitled to vote at elections. He must therefore have met the franchise qualification of owning or renting a house rated at £10; in effect, this included only the well-off.

A picture of the day-to-day business of the pharmacy at Great George Street emerges from the original prescription books, dating back to 1870. Prescriptions in these early ledgers include those for ear drops, headache preparations, cough mixtures, scalp washes, liniments (including many for animal use), enemas, eye drops, ointments, pills, suppositories and gargles, with anything from four to a dozen being dispensed each day. This recipe for cough mixture, from 1900, would not be very different if dispensed today:

Ipecacuanha wine	1 oz
Compd. Tinct. Camphor	1½ oz
Elixir vitriol	½ oz
Chloric ether	½ oz
Syr. red poppies	2 oz
Oxymel squills	2½ oz

Mix for mixture.

Whether the "Cure for rheumatism", from the same ledger, would be efficacious is more doubtful:

Turkey rhubarb	$^1/_8$ oz
Gum Guaiacum	¼ oz
Nitre	½ oz
Sulphur	½ oz
Flour of mustard	½ oz

Dose: a teaspoonful in a wineglassful of water at bedtime for 3 consecutive nights.

Recipes for non-medicinal items are to be found, too, such as hair washes, and this one "for rough hands":

Juice of 2 lemons
2 oz (4 tablespoons) Glyc[erine].
½ oz (1 tablespoon) Olive oil
1 oz (2 tablespoons) Eau de Cologne or Whisky
10 drops strong ammonia

Pour some into palm of hand before drying and after rinsing, rub well in and dry in the ordinary way.

7

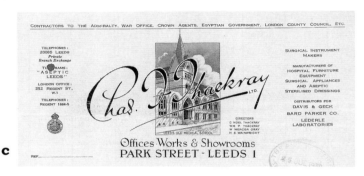

2. Letter headings spanning more than a century show both the development of typographical styles and the increase in the firm's activities:
a. A memorandum from Samuel Taylor.
b. Thackray's first printed stationery, including the information that Charles Thackray has come from Squire & Son, chemists to the royal family.
c. A new logo was designed when Thackray's became a limited company in 1935. Note the increase in their range of activities.
d. In the 1960s a more modern, sans serif typeface was adopted.
e. With greater awareness of marketing and the introduction of glossy literature in the 1970s, a new company logo was designed.

Taylor's ledgers provide an interesting insight into social attitudes of the time. Doctors' prescriptions were copied into the pharmacist's ledger and, while some patients are named, others are listed simply as "Mrs So-and-So's cook, nurse, housekeeper or servant". Children receive similar treatment, listed only as "child" or "baby". Indeed, one prescription in 1889 is for "Mrs Thackray's child", very likely twelve-year-old Charles, who had been living until the year before with his parents just over the road.

CHAPTER 2

The Founders

Charles F. Thackray

Samuel Taylor's shop would have been familiar to Charles Thackray as a boy, as it was on the opposite corner to his father's butcher's premises at 43 Great George Street (then on the corner of Oxford Row), where Charles was born and where he lived until he was eleven.

A little about Charles's parents can be gleaned from the City Library's records. His father, also Charles, had been living in Great George Street at least since 1871, with premises at nearby 13 Oxford Row. Already widowed, though aged only twenty-eight, Thackray senior's household at that time included his unmarried sister, Henrietta, Jarvis Wells, his business partner, five lodgers and two servants. He later married Mary Ann Green, who gave birth to Charles on 4th April, 1877. The family continued to live at 43 Great George Street until 1888, when they moved to Harehills View, Cowper Street, New Leeds; the butcher's shop remained, with additional premises acquired in 1892 near Kirkgate Market at 44 Fleet Street, and in 1894 at 34, 35 and 50 Fleet Street. Clearly, the business was doing well and enabled Charles senior to send his son to Giggleswick School in January 1892, at the age of fourteen, where he stayed until August 1893.

After leaving school, Charles began an apprenticeship in pharmacy at the Bradford firm of F.M. Rimmington & Son and attended lectures at Bradford Technical College. The interior of Rimmington's, in Bridge Street, remains much the same today, with its bottles, or shop-rounds, displayed on polished mahogany shelves and drawers labelled in Latin.

Records of Thackray's apprenticeship are unfortunately no longer available, but an insight into how he would have spent his time at Rimmington's is provided by the following account published in 1902 as part of a paper for discussion in *Chemist and Druggist*, the trade journal for private chemists:

"Suppose we take a boy, and the indentures have been

signed for four years. Our shops or pharmacies vary very much in character, but all need a deal of cleaning and keeping tidy, so that we cannot do better than instil the cleaning and tidying habit into the boy at the start. Alongside of this the boy should be taught to be a keen observer, making 'mental' notes often, for it is the accumulation of little facts that is required to turn out the exact and model chemist and druggist.

"We really cannot explain much technically until the boy has been with us for some six months, and has taken his turn at dusting the shop-rounds many a time, and has learned that 'Tinct.camph. co.' means 'paregoric', that it is light brown in colour, and has a pleasant smell, which he recognises as aniseed; that *cupri sulphas* is blue, and that *ferri sulphas* is green. During a few moments of each day

3. A page from the Leeds section of Bennett's *Business Directory of Yorkshire* for 1900. Both listed are Samuel Taylor's pharmacy and Jarvis Wells' butcher's shop on the opposite corner at 43 Great George Street, where Charles lived with his family until the age of eleven.

we could whet the observing appetite of the youth by comments upon the articles he so frequently handles. We might tell him why the name 'copperas' is applied, and that dragon's blood is not the blood of a dragon, but a product of the vegetable kingdom. Before this stage even he might have been keeping up his knowledge of Latin by declining in full *magnesii sulphas, spiritus chloroformi,* and *tinctura belladonnae*, with observations on the special declension to which each word belongs. How many candidates trip on *spiritus*, and little points of Latin grammar! The apprentice could be set to write fully the declension of such irregular words as calomel, aloes, enema etc.

"During the early stage, also, the youth should be shown the use of the label-damper, twine box, sealing-wax etc - points that seem nothing in themselves, but of considerable importance, as the improper use of any might go far to impress any examiner or master subsequently. How many assistants use the label-damper? I have been told that marks are deducted at the Minor examination if a candidate use his tongue. Many seem to think it clever to break twine with the finger, each operation meaning the loss of several inches of twine. Many use the teeth as a cork presser; some, when dispensing, shake up a mixture by putting a forefinger over the neck of the bottle instead of using a cork. In pouring liquids from one vessel to another how much is frequently spilled through carelessness! Do we notice that many spill nitric acid and such like on their hands? No; the substance itself acts as a warning.

"A youth should be trained in exactitude from the commencement ... by explaining to him what these little points mean when he faces an examiner he will be encouraged not to overlook any of them."

We can assume that the young Charles was "trained in exactitude" while at Rimmington's, as he followed his apprenticeship by joining Squire & Sons, Queen Victoria's official chemists, in the West End of London. Charles's daughter, Freda, recalls his pride at having taken parcels to Buckingham Palace.

He continued in pharmacy with a spell working in St Moritz, Switzerland, and St Raphael in the South of France. Contemporary trade journals show a surprising degree of interest in

12

European practice at this time, with regular features on smart Continental pharmacies, illustrated by photographs of shop interiors and window displays. Gaining experience abroad, as Charles did, was nonetheless not common practice; it was probably seen by Charles's father as rounding off his son's education, much as parents who can afford it would do today.

To qualify for registration as a pharmaceutical chemist, Thackray had to pass the Minor and Major examinations set by the Pharmaceutical Society of Great Britain, "a great terror to most young men", according to accounts at the time. Subjects of examination included physics and chemistry, botany and materia medica - the recognition and evaluation of plants and drugs listed in the British Pharmacopoeia. Candidates also had to be able to interpret prescriptions, detect errors and render them in good Latin.

Thackray sat his Major examination in the summer of 1899 over two concentrated days, involving a three-hour paper in the morning and another in the afternoon. Below is a selection of questions from the papers he sat, and passed.

Physics: Describe the construction of Bunsen's ice calorimeter and explain the method of carrying out experiments with it.

What method might be adopted with a view to determining the temperature of liquid hydrogen at boiling point? Explain the principle of the method you mention.

Chemistry: Explain fully why the molecular weight of a substance is equal to twice its vapour density.

Describe fully any single method for preparing lactic acid in quantity. What is obtained by heating lactic acid (a) alone, (b) with fuming hydriodic acid, (c) with hydrobromic acid?

Materia medica:
Name the chief commercial varieties of ipecacuanha root with their botanical and geographical sources. How would you determine the value of a given sample for pharmaceutical use?

13

What are the chief constituents of the following, and what steps would you take to ascertain whether given samples of each were of good quality: podophyllum, rhubarb, linseed, stramonium leaves, valerian root, henbane leaves?

By the time Charles Thackray sat his qualifying examinations at the turn of the century, the profession of pharmacy had clearly emerged from traditional herbalism, a change that had begun with the creation of the Pharmaceutical Society in 1841 and the Pharmacy Act of 1852, which made provision for the

4. The Pharmaceutical Society's certificate, measuring nearly 30 x 20 inches (75 x 50 cm), awarded to Charles Thackray on passing his qualifying examinations in July 1899.

Society to keep a register all chemists and druggists. The Society played a major role, too, in producing a national British Pharmacopoeia in 1864 which for the first time rationalised the thousands of different recipes - some spurious - which dispensers had relied on for their preparations. Many dispensers had actually been little better qualified than the customers they served, until 1868 when it became illegal to dispense poisons or to use the title of chemist, druggist or pharmacist unless registered with the Society, i.e. to have passed their examinations.

In 1902, three years after qualifying, Charles, with his friend Scurrah Wainwright, bought his own business, as we shall see in more detail later. The following year, he married Helen Pearce, daughter of a leading Leeds jeweller. Their first son, Charles Noel, was born on Christmas day 1905, followed by William Pearce (Tod) two years later, then Douglas in 1909 and a daughter, Freda, two years after that. (Tod's nickname, by which he had been known since childhood, derives from a popular novel of the time called *Helen's Babies*, in which one of the babies of the title was an engaging little character named Toddie or Tod.) Charles and Helen Thackray had another daughter, but frail health - caused by a weak heart, Freda recalled - meant that she went about in a bath chair, could never go to school and died when she was only ten. We can only guess at what effect the little girl's death had on Charles, but it might go some way to explaining the "mental anxiety" from which he was later to suffer.

Charles and Helen Thackray lived with their family in Roundhay, first in Davie's Avenue, then at 35 The Drive; by 1917 they had moved round the corner, to a house in The Avenue called Hill Top, and in the early Twenties the family moved to Oakwood, a Georgian mansion (now a nursing home) close to Roundhay Park.

Like Samuel Taylor, his predecessor at the Great George Street shop, Charles Thackray moved to bigger and better houses as his business prospered, and he and his family were comfortably off.

They employed a full-time chauffeur and gardener, a live-in nanny and maid (who stayed with the family 47 and 27 years respectively), a cleaner two or three mornings a week and a seamstress who made all the family's clothes, in a room set aside for the purpose, on her weekly visits.

15

A man in Charles Thackray's position would be expected to join a professional men's club. But the obvious choice, The Leeds Club, refused him membership on the grounds that he had committed the cardinal sin of being "in trade". Along with others barred for the same reason, including Snowden Schofield, founder of the Leeds department store which was to bear his name, and a couple of others in the clothing business, he set up a club of his own, which they called The West Riding Club. It had its premises on the first floor of what is now the Norwich Union building in City square.

Much of Charles's time there was spent playing bridge which, along with golf (he achieved a handicap of 8), was his abiding passion. His daughter Freda recalls that family holidays were always planned with a golf course in mind and thinks that her mother, in common with many other women of her generation, felt herself to be a golf and bridge widow. Charles was fond of singing, too, and the family often joined in singsongs round the grand piano at home.

Henry Scurrah Wainwright

Thackray's financial partner, Henry Scurrah Wainwright, was the same age as his friend Charles and, like him, was Leeds born and bred. (The name Scurrah, by which he was always known, derived from an earlier generation of the family who had moved from Well, near Ripon, to become - coincidentally - butchers in Leeds, like the Thackrays.) Scurrah Wainwright started life in Freehold Street, off the York Road, but he soon moved with his parents to Althorp Villa in Spencer Place, which in those days was untarnished by the unsalubrious reputation it has today.

The son of a glass merchant, he was sent to Western College, Harrogate, at the age of eight, where he showed promise, but his father's death when Scurrah was eleven left his mother bereft and she brought him back to be with her in Leeds. He continued his education for a year at Leeds High School in Cookridge Street and then, from the ages of thirteen to sixteen (1890-94), at Leeds Grammar School.

On leaving school, he became articled to William Adgie, Junior, at Beevers and Adgie, a leading Leeds firm of chartered accountants in Albion Street (now part of KPMG, Peat Marwick).

16

He qualified in 1899, the same year that his friend Thackray achieved his professional qualification in pharmacy, and became a partner in Beevers and Adgie in 1905.

Wainwright, like Thackray, married a local girl. She was Emily White, whose father was an importer and manufacturer of botanic medicines - a herbalist rather than a pharmacist. The family business was largely built on the success of Kompo, their patent medicine for colds. Scurrah and Emily Wainwright had one son, Richard, born in 1918, who was later to become financial director of the Thackray business and Liberal MP for Colne Valley in the Yorkshire Pennines.

Scurrah Wainwright's active involvement in Leeds life was impressive. He became President of the Leeds Society of Chartered Accountants and, apart from his association with Thackray's, he was a long-serving Director of Jowett & Sowry Ltd, Printers and the Hotel Metropole (Leeds) Ltd. He was also associated with the Leeds Tradesmen's Benevolent Association for more than 60 years (as Joint Hon. Sec. for 33 of them), was a member of the Board of Managers of the Leeds Public Dispensary and Hon. Treasurer of East Moor Approved School. As the

5. Charles F. Thackray (left) and Henry Scurrah Wainwright were both aged twenty-five when they went into partnership. The photograph of Scurrah was probably taken not long before the pair bought Taylor's pharmacy in 1902.

first Chairman appointed to the National Assistance Board's Advisory Committee for the Leeds area in 1938, he achieved the monumental task of interviewing every unemployed man under 30 years of age in the city in an effort to help them find jobs, for which he was appointed Officer of the Order of the British Empire by King George VI in 1939.

Brought up as a committed Methodist, Scurrah Wainwright devoted much time to the work of the Lady Lane Central Mission in their efforts to alleviate the abject misery which existed in the Quarry Hill area of Leeds. He was also closely associated with the organisation of the Leeds Flower Show for 40 years at which he won gold medals; the flower borders in his garden at Adel brought hundreds of visitors to see an extensive collection of herbaceous plants, especially delphiniums.

Wainwright was a shrewd investor with the ability to spot potential in an individual or an idea. A few years after backing Thackray in their joint business venture, he met an engineer named Hardy who had invented a universal joint for use in car engines. This idea had far-reaching applications and, seeing its possibilities, Wainwright encouraged his young brother-in-law to invest in the firm producing it. The Hardy-Spicer universal joint was a success; the firm prospered and eventually became an important part of what is now the giant GKN.

CHAPTER 3

Purchase of the Business

As young men, Charlie and Scurrah, as they were known to friends, lived within easy walking distance of each other's homes in New Leeds, a pleasant residential area on the east side of Chapeltown Road. It was then a more prosperous, middle-class neighbourhood than it is today, with large houses set in well-kept gardens and spacious public parks.

As Scurrah's diary for the year 1902 shows, he and Charles met at least twice a week with other friends to play cards, snooker and ping-pong in the winter, and to go for walks and play tennis at nearby Potternewton Park in the summer months. Solo whist seems to have been their particular favourite, and diary entries such as "lost 2/7" or "won 6/10" are common. Thackray regularly joined the Wainwright household for Sunday tea and chapel, and on one occasion the two went to Bridlington for a weekend's fishing and to Wetherby races in a landau.

Tennis dances and whist drives feature in their social lives; visits to the theatre are recorded, too: "Saw Irving and Terry in *Merchant of Venice* at The Grand", and "Saw Gillette in *Sherlock Holmes*". Wainwright records a week in Paris with a couple of friends; they went sightseeing and to the Folies Bergère, returning via London where they saw international music hall stars, Dan Leno and George Robey, at the Pavilion.

The diary gives a picture of two young men, both recently qualified in their chosen professions, living in Leeds at a time of tremendous expansion. "Never have I visited a city that was noisier, or one more busy and thriving," wrote the novelist Rider Haggard at the time. In a climate, then, of optimism and business confidence, it was natural that they should have ambitions to start their own business. They saw their opportunity when Samuel Taylor's pharmacy came up for sale.

To assess the potential of Taylor's business, as Thackray and Wainwright must have done, let us look at how Great George Street had developed during the nineteenth century.

19

6. The pharmacy, left, with Leeds Town Hall in the background. The shop was ideally situated in the busy shopping thoroughfare of Great George Street, opposite the Infirmary and on a route between the hospital and the doctors' consulting rooms in Park Square.

By 1869, the Gothic façade of the newly built Leeds General Infirmary dominated the north side of the street, as it does today, and many medically-related businesses had grown up in the vicinity.

In 1872, ten years after Samuel Taylor had set up shop, an oculist had opened for business next door, going by the name of the Leeds Eye Dispensary, and by 1886 a Mrs Ellen Kempner had begun her business as a surgical instrument and artificial limb maker. When the oculist moved up the road to new premises in 1894, his place was taken by the Leeds Homeopathic Dispensary; three years later, another oculist and aurist set up business on the corner of Park Street. A further surgical instrument maker opened in 1899, with the addition in the next couple of years of a drug company and a "specialist in artificial teeth".

Entries in Kelly's Directory of Leeds show what a varied and busy thoroughfare Great George Street had become by 1902 and number 70, on the apex formed by the junction with Portland Street, was a prime site.

7. The Infirmary, opened in 1868. The pharmacy is on the extreme right of the picture.

It was not only opposite the new Infirmary but also on a route between the hospital and Park Square, where many physicians had their consulting rooms. In addition, there were half a dozen private nursing homes in the vicinity, all providing potential customers. The dispensing side of the business looked healthy, too. Taylor's prescription books between 1890 and 1901 record between six and a dozen prescriptions dispensed each day.

It is worth noting that a successful chain of cut-price chemists, Taylor's Drug Company (no connection with Samuel), had been operating in Leeds for the last quarter of the nineteenth century; by 1903 they had twenty branches in the city. Boots had also opened a dazzling new shop in Briggate and another in King Edward Street. However, both these firms catered to the competitive discount market for patent medicines and a whole range of non-pharmaceutical goods. Samuel Taylor's shop, by contrast, was an up-market pharmaceutical chemist's. Thackray and Wainwright are therefore unlikely to have felt that either of the big chains represented a threat to their business prospects.

Scurrah Wainwright recorded the purchase of the Great George Street business in his diary. The entry for Friday, 25th

April, 1902 reads: "CFT arranged price of Taylor business. £900 + 13 wks at £5." Then on 19th May, Whit Monday: "CFT commenced business @ 70 Great George Street."

Two days after opening for business, Wainwright records: "Opened bank a/c for CFT. Gave him cq £100 deposit for Sam. Taylor; put £50 in his bank a/c. CFT signed contract agreeing to purchase ST's business (£900). Evg. Tennis on grass courts. 1st this year. At CFT's shop re books. CFT stayed [at HSW's] all night."

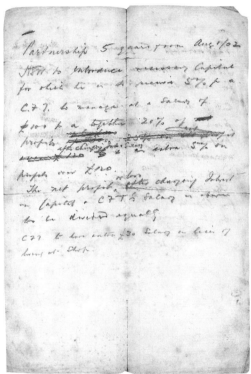

8. Scurrah Wainwright's pencilled draft (which was written on the back of one of Samuel Taylor's memorandum sheets) for a partnership agreement with Charles Thackray.

"Partnership 5 years from Aug 1/02. HSW to introduce necessary Capital for which he is to receive 5% p.a. CFT to manage at a salary of £100 p.a together 20% of profits after charging int. Salary is an extra 5% on profits over £120.

The net profit or loss, after charging Interest on Capital & CFT's salary as above is to be divided equally.

CFT to have an extra £30 salary in lieu of living at shop."

The following evening Scurrah stayed at the shop until 8.30 pm and several late evenings of bookkeeping are recorded in the ensuing weeks. One evening in August he notes: "Saw S. [Emily, his fiancée, known as Sis], then worked late at CFT's shop, 7.30-9.30, then with Mr A. [Mr Adgie] until 11.30 pm." The same month a partnership was officially agreed between the pair, the original pencil draft of which is reproduced opposite. Note that Thackray was entitled to an extra £30 salary in lieu of living over the shop.

The business traded under the name of Chas F. Thackray. Wainwright might have added his name but for the fact that chartered accountancy was a relatively new profession - the Society having received its charter in 1880 - and if accountants were seen to be involved in commercial ventures, their professional impartiality could be jeopardised.

Occupying a corner site in Great George Street, the shop had the advantage of presenting two sides to the public, each of which could display slogans: "All patent medicines at store prices"; "Wholesale and photography"; "Natural mineral waters". Although it was considered to be a high-class chemist under Samuel Taylor's supervision, Thackray and Wainwright still felt that some improvements were necessary. They immediately spent just over £40 on painting and repairs, as the ledger for the first year's business shows; further expenditure on improvements (when the buying power of £1 was equivalent to about £40 today) included:

Oak bookcase	£11 - 1 - 3
Showcase	£ 1 - 10 - 0
Bedding	£ 2 - 0 - 0
Linoleum	£ 6 - 13 - 6
Electric bell	£ 10 - 6

Two apprentices were taken on in that first year, too. A half-year payment of £20 is shown from a Mr J. Hayes in July and of £32 10s from Mr Hemingway.

The ledger gives the new business's bankers as Halifax Commercial Bank and mentions a deposit account with Camwal. (Camwal were mineral water manufacturers who supplied and replenished Thackray's, among others, with soda siphons.) Miscellaneous expenditure included:

Telephone rent for 1st year	£ 10 - 3 - 7	
Stamps	£ 6 - 11 - 0	
Labels	£17 - 13 - 6	
Packaging	£ 1 - 10 - 6	
Stationery	£ 56 - 2 - 8	
Jowett & Sowry	14 - 0	
Circulars	£ 4 - 13 - 6	

Listed under sundries were:

Coal, supplied by Carter	£ 1 - 0 - 0	
Meat, Wells	£ 4 - 0 - 0	
Groceries, Nicholls	£ 1 - 16 - 6	
Wilson	17 - 6	
Bosomworth	£ 2 - 17 - 8	
Ale, Tetley & Son	£ 1 - 16 - 6	

It was usual in those days for apprentices to live over the shop, which accounts for the food and drink orders. Note that the meat came from the butcher's opposite - Thackray's father's old business.

The following year's accounts, 1903/4, show the business's first investment in equipment: £5 12s spent on a Humanized Milk Plant Separator, plus three shillings on bottles, and sterilizing apparatus, for which no figure is shown. Profit for that year was just over £226.

In 1904/5, improvements to heating were made at a cost of £10 2s, a travelling bag was purchased for £1 5s, and two guineas were spent on advertising. Profits increased to £304, rising to £336 in 1905/6, a year in which the business bought a bicycle for £2 14s and sold the Humanized Milk Plant Separator for £2.

The following financial year, 1906/7, saw profits increased to £383, despite fairly substantial spending. A total of £142 19s was paid for new windows for the shop, a sterilizer was purchased from Manlove Alliott of Nottingham for £81, and a typewriter for £7; £36 8s 10d was spent on having catalogues printed by Jowett & Sowry, £4 14s 6d of which was offset by Parke Davis's buying advertising space in the catalogue. A further £2 that year was paid by Allen & Hanbury for a window display. At this time, too, Thackray began selling drugs wholesale and sending out standard order cards for supplies to doctors and hospitals throughout Yorkshire.

Profits for the financial year 1907/8 rose to just under £400, a total which, for the first time, was split two-thirds to Charles Thackray and one-third to Scurrah Wainwright, as opposed to the equal division they had shared previously. No doubt the extra income would have been welcome to Charles, now a family man with a wife, two sons and domestic wages to pay.

First developments

The advance of aseptic surgery in the early years of the twentieth century led to a new demand for sterilized dressings and instruments. Responding to this development, Thackray had purchased the sterilizer referred to in the accounts, Manlove Alliott's "Steam Disinfecter". This sizeable piece of equipment had to be hoisted up through the first-floor window at Great George Street and was, incidentally, dropped in the process, though it says something for the manufacturer that it came to no harm.

Thackray could now develop another side to his business, supplying sterilized dressings to the Leeds General Infirmary, the nearby Women's and Children's Hospital and neighbouring nursing homes. Further income was derived from leasing part of his premises to the Yorkshire Pathological Service, where the Gough brothers (a surgeon and gynaecologist), carried out pathological investigations for general practitioners. The Infirmary's accounts record the sum of 10s 6d being paid to Thackray for this service.

By 1908 the first powered transport was acquired, a Triumph motorcycle costing £48 - an amount the firm could well afford in a year when profits rose to nearly £752, more than three times the total for the second year of business. The motorbike, Charles Thackray's daughter, Freda, recalls, used to be wheeled up a plank to be stored overnight in the kitchen of the family house in Roundhay. Cars do not make an appearance in the company's accounts until 1922, when a Swift was purchased, an open-topped tourer that had belonged to Scurrah Wainwright and his wife, and a year later a 10 horsepower Singer for one of the firm's travellers in London.

The year 1908 also marked Thackray's first advertising in a

25

9. The "steam disinfecter", bought in 1906 at a cost of £81. Thackray's could now sterilize dressings and instruments for nearby hospitals and nursing homes.

nationally distributed publication, with two advertisements placed in *Chemist & Druggist* at a cost of 3s 6d each.

The first available prescription book for the business under Thackray's ownership is dated 1909 (the ledger for this year was supplied by Jowett & Sowry, the Leeds printers of which Wainwright was a director). Ear and eye drops, ointments, mouthwashes, nasal sprays and cough mixtures continued to be dispensed, mostly at a charge of between 9d and 2/6. Hey's dentifrice cost 1/3, as did cough mixture; a prescription for the lenses only for a pair of pince-nez was dispensed at a cost of eight shillings, and a pair of gold-filled (rolled gold) spectacle frames for 8/6, and their lenses, four shillings.

The use of Latin in prescription-writing was still widely evident in the 1909 ledger too: *"Solve et fiat mistura"*, Dissolve and make into a mixture, and *"T bis die si opus sit"*, Take twice a day if needed. Customers to the shop represented a wide range of social class, from Lady Harewood, whose name appears in the ledger for 1910, to maids and servants.

The doctors whose prescriptions are written in the early ledgers are overwhelmingly from Park Square practices; many of them also worked at the Infirmary and would pass the Great George Street shop en route between hospital and consulting rooms. Not only did these physicians send their patients to the shop, but they also had accounts there themselves (which, incidentally, meant that they could add wine to their bills and their wives could buy expensive perfumes and cosmetics, too). A large number of these medical men became lifelong friends of Charles Thackray and their role in his success should not be underestimated. They helped the Thackray name to be known in Leeds and later all over Yorkshire. Many of them were young and at the beginning of their careers, and they played an important part in the development of the surgical instrument business in which Thackray collaborated closely with the doctors.

The first tangible evidence of Thackray's relationship with the Infirmary comes from the House Committee Minutes Book for 1910, in which their monthly expenditure is recorded. In November of that year, the sum of £29 was paid for operating gloves, an innovation in British surgery brought to Leeds after a visit to the United States by the famous surgeon at the Infirmary, Berkeley Moynihan. It was Moynihan, too, who introduced to Leeds the practice of wearing a white coat while operating, despite being ridiculed at the time.

The gloves must have proved successful, for £27 9s 0d was paid for a further batch the following month, and regular payments to Thackray's for operating gloves, ranging from £18 to £52, feature in the succeeding hospital accounts. Nowadays, it comes as something of a surprise to learn that Thackray's used to repair the gloves, a practice that continued in some hospitals until as late as the 1960s.

In 1908 Thackray sold his first surgical instruments, supplied by Selby of London. The instruments side of the business grew so rapidly that two years later he set up an instrument repairs department in Portland Street, at the back of the pharmacy. Compared to prescription fees, charged in shillings and pence, the income from instrument repairs was in a different league altogether. In September 1915, for example, the Infirmary paid Thackray's £95 11s 3d for repairs, a sizeable sum in those days; a further £53 9s 8d was paid in October and amounts of more than £100 each are recorded in consecutive months the following year. With such large sums involved, it is likely that the hospital was refurbishing its entire stock of polished carbon steel instruments to plated equipment.

The early years of Thackray's business coincided with major advances in surgical techniques. Leeds, in particular, was a renowned centre of high-calibre surgeons. Many had made their name at the Infirmary; best known of all was Berkeley George Andrew Moynihan. He had trained in Leeds, became a house surgeon at the Infirmary and was Professor of Surgery there between 1910 and 1927. From 1926 to 1931 he was President of the Royal College of Surgeons. He achieved world-wide recognition for his contribution to abdominal surgery and every conceivable honour: KB, CB, KCMG, Baronet and finally a hereditary peerage.

In diplomatic circles it is sometimes said that KCMG stands for "kindly call me god"; in medicine in Moynihan's day, this description was not far off the mark as applied to surgeons. Indeed, in February 1910 the Infirmary's House Committee records a complaint from Mr Moynihan and his colleague Mr Lawford Knaggs, about the inadequacy of theatre accommodation. By May, architects' plans for new theatres were prepared. Surgeons asked for what they wanted and expected to get it. If they needed an instrument for a particular surgical technique, they would have it made to their own requirements. It was Moynihan who first suggested to Charles Thackray that he should make instruments; and the firm, with its experience in repairs at their premises just across the road from the Infirmary, was well placed to do so.

Moynihan's skill as a surgeon was undisputed. He was fond of saying, "A good surgeon must have an eagle's eye, a lion's heart and a lady's hand ..." although, ironically, he required Thackray's to make instruments with larger than average bows (the rings forming the handles of scissors, forceps and so on) to fit his fingers comfortably. A bronze of Moynihan's hands, displayed in the University's medical and dental school library, bears this out.

In 1908, Thackray took on his first representative, Noel Farley, who was to play an important part in developing the firm's business. By 1914, he had taken on two more, both qualified pharmacists: Merryweather Shaw (who went on to complete more than 50 years' service) and William Mercer Gray, who later became Managing Director.

As had become customary in the firm, Mercer Gray joined by way of recommendation, in this case by Merryweather Shaw's brother, Granville. Mr Merryweather Shaw recounted the story of how his brother was visiting the Great George Street shop when Charles Thackray asked him if he knew of any suitable young pharmacist who would act as a representative. Granville Shaw knew Mercer Gray personally as he had often entertained the Shaws at their house in Manchester with his singing (he was later Vice-President of The Leeds Amateur Operatic Society) and recommended him.

The decision to take on new representatives marks the beginning of a shift in emphasis from the retail side of the business towards wholesaling. The firm enjoyed regular orders for drugs and equipment from Yorkshire hospitals, but representatives now had to break new ground and compete with long-established names in the field if the firm were to expand. Charles Thackray's insistence on employing only qualified pharmacists as salesmen resulted in a sales force well above the average. And in the days when university degrees and professional qualifications were less widespread than they are today, the letters MPS (Member of the Pharmaceutical Society) after a name went a good way towards overcoming any prejudice surgeons might have in talking to a sales representative.

29

CHAPTER 4

The First World War

By the outbreak of the First World War, turnover of the business was about six times that of the first financial year. Thackray's was employing 25 people, including eight instrument makers and three full-time representatives. The shift in emphasis of the business from retailing towards wholesale and manufacturing of pharmaceuticals and dressings meant that Chas F. Thackray became recognised throughout the North of England as a major distributor of a broad range of surgical supplies.

Representatives visited customers over a wide area, supplying wholesale pharmaceuticals not only to hospitals and nursing homes but also to general practitioners serving rural areas. Where chemist shops were few and far between, doctors dispensed many of their own prescriptions and therefore carried stocks of common medicines, such as cough mixtures, indigestion remedies and so on, with them. Customers grew to know their Thackray's representatives, and trusted their advice.

The First World War inevitably took a lot of men away from their jobs, and pharmacists were no exception to begin with, but in 1915, after many applications to government departments, they were placed on the "starred" list of indispensable workers. However, after the introduction of conscription in 1916, there was some resentment in the profession that Army authorities gave pharmacists no definite rank "suited to their educational attainments".

War naturally stimulated demand for dressings, many of which were sewn on to bandages by hand in those days. Thackray's, looking to boost their production and not afraid to pioneer new methods, bought a machine which made the "Washington Haigh field dressing" cheaply and quickly.

The acceptance by the War Office of Thackray's "Aseptic" range as standard field dressings was important to the firm, both ensuring large war contracts for drugs and sundries and, to a lesser extent, instruments. Ministry approval also provided a useful testimonial to potential customers.

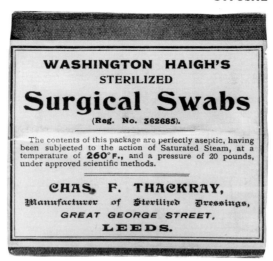

WASHINGTON HAIGH'S
STERILIZED
Surgical Swabs
(Reg. No. 362685).

The contents of this package are perfectly aseptic, having been subjected to the action of Saturated Steam, at a temperature of **260°F.**, and a pressure of 20 pounds, under approved scientific methods.

CHAS. F. THACKRAY,
Manufacturer of Sterilized Dressings,
GREAT GEORGE STREET,
LEEDS.

10. Surgical swabs, part of the Washington Haigh range which was profitable for the firm in the First World War.

The Leeds General Infirmary continued to place regular orders with the firm and in 1916 the hospital ordered sterilizers to equip its new operating theatres in the King Edward VII Memorial Extension. The minutes of the building committee, chaired by Charles Lupton, and with the surgeon Mr Secker Walker present, read as follows:

"On the request of the surgeons, it was decided to obtain from the Kny-Scheerer Manufacturing Co. of New York, through Mr C.F. Thackray, the following sterilizers for the new theatres. The 12 copper cylinders and 1 cylinder sterilizer not to be ordered until after the war."

The total for the ten items of sterilizing equipment, including water, instrument and glove sterilizers, dishes, copper cylinders and a cylinder sterilizer, was £535 13s 0d (worth about £17,500 today).

The following year, in April, 1917, another substantial order was placed by the hospital for theatre furniture:

"2 Operation tables, Universal Model   @ £35   70 0 0
2 Operation tables, Universal Model
with modified head piece   @ £40   80 0 0
2 Operation tables, Surgical O.P.
[Out Patients] as Down's Fig. 9586

31

with double rack	@ £13	26	0 0
1 Operation table O.P. Ophthalmic	@ £11	11	0 0
5 Special instrument cupboards	@ £24	120	0 0
1 Instrument cupboard O.P.	@ £13	13	0 0
5 Full curved instrument tables for Sister's use	@ £11	55	0 0
7 Instrument tables	@ £6 10s	45	10 0
3 Revolving basin stands	@ £2 2s	6	6 0
14 Stools	@ £1 10s	21	0 0
5 Anaesthetic tables	@ £3 15s	18	15 0
1 Instrument tray stand	@ £3 10s	3	10 0
24 Towel rails	@ 10s 6d	12	12 0
1 Perfection operating lamp as Curry & Paxton's fig. 39	@ £4 15s	4	15 0
	Total £	487	8 0"

Note that competitors' catalogue references were given in a couple of cases; in the absence of a comprehensive catalogue of Thackray's own, this was common practice by hospitals placing orders.

ADVERTISEMENTS   919

A New Portable Operating Table

THIS table is mainly constructed of an alloy of aluminium combining strength and durability with lightness.
It is easily unfolded and erected. The lifting movement is carried out in finest quality steel.
WEIGHT.—24 lbs.; with Accessories and Case, 34 lbs.
SIZE.—In position, 6 ft. long, 18½ ins. wide, 33 ins. high; folded in case 41 ins. long, 23 ins. wide, 5½ ins. high.

Foot and head pieces are quickly fixed at any angle. Trendelenburg position is automatically obtained by turning handle shown in illustration.

Patent app. No. 15725—13

Cost of Table, complete with Stirrups, £15 15s. 0d. Case 30s. extra.

CHAS. F. THACKRAY
Surgical Instrument Maker, **LEEDS.**

11. Wright's Medical Annual of 1914 illustrates some of the equipment Thackray's was supplying at the time. This folding operating table, designed for Sir Berkeley Moynihan, was supplied to doctors who carried out "lumps and bumps" surgery (such as removal of cysts and polyps, tonsils and adenoids) in patients' homes.

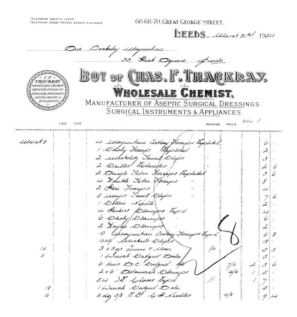

12. Invoice to Sir Berkeley Moynihan. One item, (line19) was for the repair of 54 india rubber gloves, a practice that continued as late as the 1960s.

The Infirmary's accounts continue to show instrument repairs undertaken by Thackray's until 1926, at which point the practice of itemising their monthly expenditure was discontinued, and a total only given.

Thackray's employed fourteen instrument makers by the end of the war in 1918, out of a total workforce that had risen to 32. The surgical equipment side of the business prospered, largely owing to the increase in surgery in Leeds and, realising that there was a limit to the amount of wholesale drug business that could be obtained from family doctors, Thackray decided to concentrate on medical and surgical supplies to hospitals. By 1921, Chas F. Thackray was included in the list of Leeds Chamber of Commerce members under "Scientific Instrument Makers".

The war years saw the sales area for instruments greatly extended. Consequently more representatives were taken on and organised into a sales team. Unlike most salesmen, they were not paid on commission, but given a share of the profits, a practice which encouraged them to win their contracts on the most favourable terms for the company. Thackray and Wainwright took meticulous care in their assessment of bonuses, considering each name individually and awarding a share of the profits according to how he had fared.

In later years, when there were many more employees to assess, the bonus scheme became a target for much criticism, giving rise to considerable resentment among those who felt they had been unfairly rewarded. Resentment was fuelled by the fact that there was no formula for assessing how much an individual had contributed to profits; and there were inevitably those who ingratiated themselves to their bosses, especially as bonus time drew near.

Thackray's reputation in the trade for having a first-class sales network throughout the UK won them important distribution rights, and they acquired agencies for various products originating in the USA. Success in this field was due in large measure to Noel Farley, whose frequent trips to America, often in the wake of Moynihan, led to the introduction of sophisti-

13. Noel Farley. He secured valuable agencies for American products in the 1920s and died unexpectedly following an appendix operation in 1932. This photograph hung in Thackray's head office for many years, although it is not clear why he is pictured on horseback.

34

cated American equipment - by then in advance of home-grown products in terms of design and gadgetry - to Britain. Among these, he secured a sole selling agency for Scanlan Morris sterilizers, an advanced design which gave Thackray's some measure of success. (A ledger for the year 1923 records Farley's travelling expenses on one such trip: £50 passage and £200 expenses.)

Noel Farley's fruitful career with the firm was cut short by his unexpected death in 1932 from septicaemia following an appendix operation at the LGI. His death at a young age shocked everyone who knew him. Apart from being an excellent representative, Farley was an exceptionally personable man. He and his wife were popular visitors to the Wainwright household, and took pleasure in giving books as presents to Scurrah's young son, Richard, especially as they had no children of their own. And when in London, Farley made a point of taking young Freda Thackray for outings from her boarding school in the Home Counties.

Through Farley's efforts, American companies, such as Davis & Geck, who manufactured soluble sutures, saw Thackray's, with its nation-wide sales network, as an ideal distributor for their products. The sutures were Thackray's first national distributorship, going right on to the operating table. They were a superb product and were to be both profitable and good for the firm's reputation. In due course, cine films were made of classic surgery being done with Davis & Geck sutures, and representatives were each equipped with a Kodak home cine projector to use with hospital audiences.

Davis & Geck's parent company, Lederle, front-runners in the 1920s in the production of serums for measles, whooping cough and other infectious diseases, also asked Thackray's to act for them throughout the UK, and provided, at their own expense, three or four more representatives for the purpose. Later, when sulphonamide drugs were introduced, Lederle again made Thackray's their UK distributor.

CHAPTER 5

Park Street

By the 1920s, the firm's changing emphasis from pharmaceuticals and dressings to surgical supply brought rapid expansion, and Thackray's outgrew its Great George Street premises. By 1926, employees had doubled in number compared with 1914, though, of these, there were still only fourteen instrument makers, the same as at the end of the war.

Pressure on space had been alleviated to some extent in 1921, when Thackray's took over nearby premises at number 35, which was opposite the shop on the south side of the street, between Oxford Place and Oxford Row. However, there was still a need for more room and Charles Thackray was fortunate to find what he was looking for just round the corner in Park Street where the Yorkshire Archaeological Society and the Thoresby Society (the Leeds historical society) occupied the Old Medical School.

Dating from 1865, the Park Street building was one of the first purpose-built medical schools in the provinces, equipped with laboratories, dissecting rooms, a museum, library, materia medica and lecture theatre. Its architect, who chose the neo-Gothic style popular at the time, was George Corson; other designs of his in Leeds include what is now the Central Library and the Grand Theatre in Briggate.

In 1884 the Leeds School of Medicine had sold the Medical School to the Yorkshire College of Science, precursor of Leeds University. When the College later built a new medical school in Thoresby Place it leased the Park Street building to the Yorkshire Archaeological Society and the Thoresby Society. After renting the premises for four years, the Yorkshire Archaeological Society bought the building in 1901 and immediately sold "a moiety [half] of the premises" to the Thoresby Society. So when Charles F. Thackray made an offer the Societies considered "too good to refuse" and acquired the property in 1926, it was appropriate that it was to have a medical use.

14. The Old Medical School in Park Street. When Thackray's took over the building in 1926 it had altered little externally since its original design in 1865 (top).

37

When Thackray's took over the building, a lot needed doing to it, as six typewritten foolscap pages of repairs and alterations listed by Leeds architects A. and F. Mosley Ltd testify. Work included replacing windows and staircases, altering internal walls and doors, removing obsolete gas fittings and dilapidated fireplaces, installing new lavatories, providing new fittings to bottle-washing, and providing new shelving and counters. The quotation for repairs, dated 1929, was for more than £3,000 worth of work, an indication of just how much needed to be done.

Administration and most of manufacturing were transferred to the new premises, no. 70 Great George Street being retained as a retail pharmacy and for the manufacture and fitting of surgical appliances; the temporary overspill into no. 35 was discontinued in 1928.

Park Street served the firm well for over half a century, a period which saw many changes to the premises. One alteration involved creating a director's suite in what had been the Medical School's Library, a tall room whose ceiling extended right into the roof rafters and which had, along two of its walls, a gallery served by a small staircase.

Aware of the building's historic significance, and foreseeing that it might one day be listed, Robert Gray (Mercer Gray's son)

15. The engraved glass doors which marked the entrance to the Park Street works from 1926. They were rescued when the building was demolished and are now displayed at the Thackray Medical Museum in Leeds.

was careful to ensure that any alteration to the library could be reversed without damage to the original. Thus a false ceiling was suspended within the cavernous interior so that directors' meetings could be held in the room created below, while access was retained, via the staircase, to instrument patterns stored in cupboards lining the walls upstairs. Entry to the staircase was closely guarded by the Managing Director's secretary during board meetings, as anyone going to the gallery upstairs was well placed to eavesdrop.

Early days at the Old Medical School in Park Street are remembered clearly by staff who worked there. One who joined Thackray's in 1928 recalled:

"I left school at fourteen and worked for a few months at Boots. Then my uncle, who worked at the Hospital for Women, suggested Thackray's. I went and knocked on the door in my short trousers and asked for a job. Mr Mercer Gray engaged me at once. For the first two or three years I did menial tasks like packing parcels and taking them to the post office.

"Mr Thackray impressed me very much. He was a very likeable chap, always smartly dressed. There was no barrier with him. It was nothing to see him take his coat off to wash bottles - Winchesters, they were called, holding three or four pints - in the basement at Park Street. I remember he had a massive office, with a massive desk in it, a contrast to the petite person who sat behind it. He travelled in a chauffeur-driven limousine, a Hudson, an American car. One of the reps had his own chauffeur, too. It saved time, he said, as he could write reports while travelling."

Mercer Gray also drove an American car, an immaculate black Buick, kept in its pristine condition with the help of young apprentices who would wash the car on Saturday mornings.

Though clearly a man his staff felt they could talk to, Chas. F. Thackray demanded high standards. As a sixteen-year-old apprentice in 1932, another retired employee recalls:

"I was scraping enamel off a trolley to be re-enamelled - this was before the days of stainless steel - and Mr Thackray came to inspect the work. He asked for some paper to be spread on the floor and he went on his hands and knees so he could check that the underside of the trolley had had the enamel properly scraped off."

The lad had been encouraged to try for a job at Thackray's by his Sunday School teacher, Miss Ackroyd, who was then Charles Thackray's secretary. Apprentices were interviewed by Mr Thackray personally. "I went along with my father and remember being struck by Mr Thackray's glasses. He was wearing two pairs and had another on his desk. I started my apprenticeship when I was sixteen and finished when I was twenty-three."

A thorough training by any standards, but the firm's reputation was built on first-class workmanship. It is fair to say that Thackray's was rated as one of the best employers in the Leeds area, an essential element in the production of high quality instruments. (Even during the Depression years of high unemployment, Thackray's were able to offer a 58 ¾ hour working week for engineers, compared to the average 51 ¾.) It is equally fair to say that the staff were exceptionally loyal and formed a closely-knit team who were willing to put themselves out on their employer's behalf when necessary. One retired employee who was with the firm all his working life, remembers annual stocktaking at Park Street:

"There was no stainless steel in those days, so kidney trays, bedpans etcetera were enamelware, and they got very dirty on the shelves. These were washed in buckets of water in the basement. Noel Thackray would come and help now and then. Every time we'd finished stocktaking, we had a bath in the tower at the top of the building, in the caretaker's area."

In those pre-computer days, stocktaking was a major undertaking, with thousands of items to be checked and counted by hand. Most of those involved will cast their eyes to the ceiling at the mention of the word stocktaking, but they will also fondly recall the comradeship it engendered; it was one of the few occasions, for instance, when directors sat drinking cups of tea with the staff.

There were other opportunities, too, for directors to work side by side with employees:

"At holiday time, Whitsuntide and Easter, the firm closed for the Monday and Tuesday. We worked with a skeleton staff and one director on the Tuesday to open the post and dispatch any urgent orders.

"We thought nothing of taking urgent orders in the car to a local hospital. Once, we had an order for six sterilizing drums -

16. Guests invited to Noel Thackray's twenty-first birthday party at Powolny's Restaurant in Leeds included friends and Thackray staff. Noel is sitting at the head of the centre table and his father, standing, is at the opposite end; on the extreme right of the picture is Noel Farley and at the head of the table nearest the camera is Mercer Gray. Edgar Blackburn is seated two places to Noel Thackray's left and, further down the table (to the left of the pillar), are Miss Ackroyd and Tod Thackray.

they're about fifteen inches tall and a foot wide - at Harrogate. The director on duty had a sports car. It was raining and, with the drums piled in my lap, we couldn't shut the roof, so we were wet through by the time we arrived. But you didn't mind."

Long-serving employees all speak of the family feeling the firm enjoyed. The recruitment of staff by recommendation rather than advertisement meant that there were several fathers and sons, and husbands and wives working for the firm. A lively calendar of social events meant that everyone knew each other, whichever department they belonged to. Herbert Winters, who had joined the firm in 1928 as a fourteen-year-old apprentice, started the Social Committee in the 1930s. He admits he did so with a view to helping retain staff, to whom he could not offer high wages. "The Social Committee was financed by raffles," he explained. "We had dances, theatre outings and whist drives, and we started a football team and played at Roundhay Park."

Others remember the dances held at the Capitol or Astoria, at which Edgar Webb, who had been Mr Thackray's chauffeur and who gave 40 years' service to the firm, acted as master of ceremonies. There were also firm's outings to Windermere and Scarborough, the Festival of Britain and trips to see the Blackpool illuminations by train, for which a special coach was reserved for Thackray's use. "In the Forties and Fifties, people used to work on Saturday mornings," staff remember, "so after work, at Saturday lunchtime, we would all walk down to City Square station."

The Social Club continued to flourish until the 1980s. Weekly subscriptions from employees and a monthly whist drive at "The Old Vic" (The Victoria Hotel), together with contributions from the firm, provided funds for dances and outings. Concerts were laid on, too. Professional artists were booked to perform at the Belgrave Hall, including a young Harry Corbett, then beginning to make a name for himself with his puppet, Sooty, while earning his living as an electrician.

The Thackray Football Team competed in Sunday Combination League matches, and a game between works and sales and marketing became an annual fixture. The success of Thackray's football team could be patchy: in the 1970s, after winning three matches in a row, the team suffered injuries to four players in a single game. (Greater success on the field was achieved by Jim Milburn, the former "iron man" of Leeds United and uncle of the famous brothers Jack and Bobby Charlton. He worked as a labourer at Beeston from 1966 to 1982.)

Cricket and golf matches were played, too, together with table tennis tournaments against local organisations, such as NALGO, British Telecom, the Post Office, Negas and Yorkshire Electricity.

CHAPTER 6

The Twenties and Thirties: First exports and a new factory

In the mid-1920s, sales in the home market were flourishing. Turnover in wholesale pharmaceuticals was brisk and increased instrument sales led to the opening of a London depot in Regent Street. Now Thackray turned his attention overseas.

Herbert Winters remembers the firm's first export order: "One day - I would have been sixteen or seventeen years old - Mr Thackray telephoned and asked me to go up to his office and bring the day book with me. On his desk were some samples. 'We're going to send this lot to Dr Geraldi in Gibraltar,' he said. That was the first dispatch we made."

Much of surgery round the world at this time was British because Empire countries sent trainees and postgraduates to this country to further their education. Therefore British products sold well in Empire countries and where there was a strong British influence, such as Canada, Australasia, South Africa, Egypt and Nigeria.

To begin with, Thackray's sent its own manufactured surgical instruments chiefly to the Mediterranean (Egypt, Malta, Cyprus), the Middle East and West Africa; they were suppliers to the Crown Agents, whose job was to buy for the Crown colonies. In those days, salesmen went on trips lasting, perhaps, six months, or up to two years. Samples were packed into a couple of cabin trunks and had to be "leap-frogged" so that they were waiting for the salesman at the right place.

By 1930 the yearly total for exports was nearly £6,000, about one thirtieth of total turnover. Markets had been built up, thanks chiefly to the efforts of Noel Farley and substantial leaflet advertising, and to the increasing renown of the "Moynihan School" of surgery. These markets were widened and consolidated during the Thirties, in large part by Sidney Beardmore, who travelled all over the world selling Thackray products. "I said good-bye to Beardmore today," wrote Scurrah Wainwright in a letter to Noel Farley's widow, Catherine, in 1933. "He is going to India and other distant places."

Thackray's employees had increased to 100 by 1931. Since 1914 the firm had trebled its production and increased its turnover despite generally slack trading conditions in most of the economy. Then international financial problems and a world slump led to devaluation of the pound. Such conditions, with fewer goods imported, made it opportune for Thackray's to expand their own manufacturing capacity.

Thus the early Thirties saw the introduction of the firm's own hospital sterilizers, operating tables and other items of theatre furniture, some of which made up the shipments to hospitals overseas. A member of the Export Department at that time explains:

"Goods were packed in cartons at Park Street. Larger items were measured and had cases made for them, by G.H. Dovener, the undertaker's. We had no means of weighing the cases - they could be as much as 10 cwt - so we took them on a handcart to Great George Street where Stansfield, the steel merchants [who supplied steel rods for instrument-making to Thackray's] had a weighbridge they let us use. There was a very steep hill behind the Park Street building, about one in four, and we had to pull the cart up snakewise, and then back down again."

At the rear of the premises was a yard from which goods left the building: "Sometimes there would be five or six railway drays, pulled by shire horses, queueing in the yard for a shipment of 30 or 40 cases. We had no means of lifting the cases on to the wagons, but we had a little pair of wheels to put underneath one edge of the case. The chap at the front would sometimes end up under the wagon. They were taken to Hunslet goods station and sent mainly to Liverpool, and sometimes London, docks."

With dozens of cases awaiting shipment, storage became a problem. "It was like sardines at Park Street. Cases were stacked on stairways and in passageways. Even the front entrance had cases in it sometimes. We took over part of Craven Dairies at the back for storing things and a basement garage at the bottom of Park Street, but a fire gutted the garage and we lost a lot of stuff ..."

To accommodate the extra manufacturing activity at the increasingly cramped Park Street site, the entire rear half of the building facing Chariot Street was demolished in 1933. It was then rebuilt to three storeys as a modern building of the time, with rigid steel girder framework and concrete floors. Later, in 1936, an extra floor was added to make it four storeys at the rear. The front of the building remained as it had when first built as the Medical School, apart from the removal of two parts of the coping on the front wall for safety reasons.

While the rebuilding in 1933 was in progress, the Wholesale Drug Department was temporarily transferred to Park Square. However, this building was burned down and the department was again moved to temporary accommodation, in Sovereign Street. (These premises were shared with Goodall & Backhouse, patent medicine distributor and relish-maker, which has led some staff to say that the smell of Yorkshire Relish will always remind them of the Drug Department.)

Although the firm rode the Depression years well, it suffered a major blow in 1934 when Charles Thackray died suddenly at the age of 57. He failed to return from an evening walk in Roundhay Park near his home and later his body was recovered from Waterloo Lake.

Thackray's widow, Helen, had witnessed his suffering from mental anxiety for the previous two years, and expressed in a letter to Mercer Gray her feeling that he would at last have found

17. Mercer Gray, who joined Thackray's before the First World War. He took over as Managing Director when Charles Thackray died in 1934.

45

peace. Scurrah Wainwright, writing to Catherine Farley, said, "He was obsessed by a conviction that he was losing his mental capacity and that it would end in the ruin of himself and everyone concerned. Actually there was little if any deterioration in his capacities except on this point which evidently preyed on his mind until it upset his mental balance."

A tendency to anxiety that seemed to run in the family and the effects of his young daughter's death were both likely to have contributed to Thackray's mental state. Nowadays, his condition would probably be diagnosed as anxiety neurosis, a common enough condition, but less widely recognised and treated sixty years ago than it is today.

Thackray died when the two of his sons who had joined the business were relatively young and inexperienced. Noel was twenty-nine and his brother, Tod, twenty-seven. (Douglas, then twenty-five, had chosen medicine as his profession and Freda did not join the firm.) Although Scurrah Wainwright had expressed his pleasure in the way that Noel was "accepting and carrying his new responsibilities" shortly after Charles Thackray's death, it was felt that the person best placed to take up the reins was Mercer Gray. He had been with Thackray's since he was a newly qualified pharmacist before the First World War and had become the most senior manager in the firm.

Ownership of Charles Thackray's share of the firm passed to Noel and Tod, and financial security was provided for Helen. (The business had grown at this time to achieve annual sales of about £200,000, equivalent to over £5 million today.) It was agreed that a limited company should be formed, with H.S. Wainwright as Chairman, Mercer Gray as Managing Director and C. Noel Thackray and W.P.(Tod) Thackray as Directors of Commercial and Manufacturing operations.

Mercer Gray takes charge

The Thirties were formative years in the field of surgery and Thackray's was designing and making an increasingly wide range of instruments. It was therefore essential for the firm to produce a comprehensive catalogue to replace the handful of leaflets (not to mention competitors' catalogues) they had relied

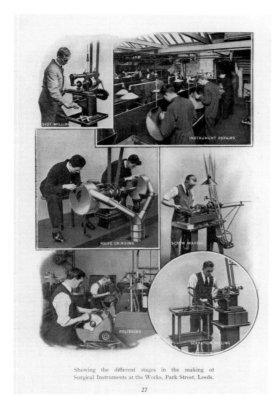

Showing the different stages in the making of Surgical Instruments at the Works, Park Street, Leeds.

27

18. Surgical instruments were hand crafted, not mass-produced. "My workshops are equipped with the most modern plant and machinery for the production of surgical instruments; the utmost care is taken to carry out the exact instructions of the Surgeon under the supervision of the principal," Charles Thackray assured customers in his preface to a pre-war catalogue from which this page is taken.

on to date. In 1937, under Mercer Gray's direction, two volumes containing line drawings of every instrument Thackray's supplied were made available to customers for the first time. This meant that hospitals could now order by Thackray's catalogue number, putting an end to the somewhat galling practice of using competitors' reference numbers on instrument orders.

From then on, the catalogue was regularly updated and reissued. Tod Thackray was put in charge of compiling these sizeable volumes, a job he carried out with painstaking care. However, in using another firm's catalogue as a model, he inadvertently copied their material to an extent that amounted to a breach of copyright. Not unreasonably in the circumstances, Thackray's were sued and the catalogues had to be replaced.

Many instruments were made to surgeons' own specifications: witness the number named after their inventor in any Thackray catalogue index. This close co-operation between surgeon and manufacturer shows up in the firm's correspondence,

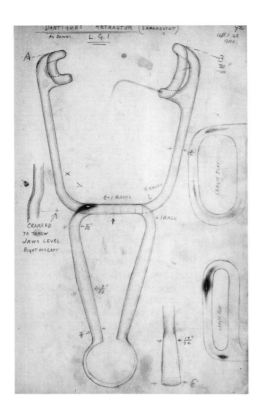

19. This page from a 1938 pattern book shows the scorch marks made when an instrument – still hot from grinding – was compared for accuracy with the drawing. Patterns were drawn in duplicate, with the bottom copy accompanying each batch made.

such as this letter from Mr Cockcroft-Barker, MB, ChB, writing to Mercer Gray in 1938 about a dilator: "The true secret of the instrument," which is not easy to decipher owing to Mr Cockcroft-Barker's handwriting, "is the *curve* and also the *length* of the dilating portion." He suggests to Mercer Gray in a post script that this "might be a good thing to keep up your own sleeve."

Sometimes surgeons came in person to Park Street to buy their instruments. One Thackray's staff member, taking his turn from clerical work to serve in what was known as "the front shop", remembers assembling a huge order for two Australian surgeons. "Because you have looked after us so efficiently and carefully," said one, "I am going to tell you about my new invention." The invention in question was the Williams screwdriver, characterised by a then revolutionary ratchet system and locking-on mechanism, which became famous in the Thackray catalogue.

Surgeons could also get to know of new products at medical exhibitions. Thackray's could claim to be the first in its field to obtain permission to run an exhibition in conjunction with a surgeons' meeting, a practice that is widespread nowadays with clear advantages to both parties.

If instruments were to be made to the high standards surgeons expected, they also had to reach them in perfect condition, so that packaging needed to be thorough and reliable. A large room at Park Street was given over to dispatch, as recalled by this employee who worked as a packer:

"There was a big square in the middle of the room where the typists prepared orders and labels. Packers used to collect a big tray with instruments on and then pack them and check them off a list. For packing, we had wood wool, brown-paper sticky tape and a large roll of corrugated paper which we had to roll down the steps from the top floor. The tally, or label, was typed, ready to stick on. When an order was packed, we used to put it on to another counter behind us, where another girl weighed and stamped them and put them into red bags for the post office."

Post was taken to the station by handcart. Young apprentices at the time well remember struggling with this unwieldy transport: "When loaded, the handcart was very heavy and its wheels got stuck in the tramlines. Trams used to come down Park Row and round the corner towards Briggate and you often found the handcart going the same way. But you were trying to go straight on across the road and sometimes you had to ask someone passing to give you a hand."

One apprentice, who had started at the age of fourteen as a packer in the export department making crates for operating tables, had always wanted to be an engineer. He was offered a transfer to work under Arthur Hallam (who, as foreman of the instrument works, was to become a key figure in developing Charnley's instrumentation) and his second-in-command, Henry Smith. "I had imagined I would be working with great big machines with sparks flying," he said, "but for the first month or so I swept the floors and went on errands to get the men fish and chips and twopenny growlers [pork pies]. Then I learnt to file instrument bows by hand."

Thackray's catalogue for this pre-war period listed about

2,500 different items (at least twenty of which were to Moynihan's design). Park Street, where all design and the majority of manufacture of instruments took place, had become totally inadequate and by the end of the decade, larger premises were urgently needed.

A new factory would have to be within tolerable reach of Park Street, so that the Managing Director, Mercer Gray, could travel to the works easily; it should not be too expensive, and should be capable of expansion. A site fulfilling these criteria became available at Viaduct Road, about a mile to the west of Park Street, as a result of the Government's wartime policy of concentrating industry to make best use of resources. Firms with more than one workplace were required to give up some of their premises and condense into what was left.

In these circumstances, Thackray's found a willing seller in Leeds Dyers, to which Scurrah Wainwright was financial adviser. They occupied an old, but solidly-built, textile dyeing works alongside the River Aire and the Leeds and Liverpool Canal. The building, on three floors, served Thackray's well - and continued to do so as the Surgery Division until 1993 - although when the firm wanted to expand the premises after the war, they could not get planning permission; it was discovered there were major sewers underground which could not be built on, and to which, anyway, access would have to be maintained. In the event, a group of Nissen huts was erected in the yard to accommodate the polishing shops. Subsequently, these were taken over by a stove enameller's with the confusingly similar name of Thacker's, who remain there today.

While the Viaduct Road site accommodated the firm's increased instrument manufacture, production of pharmaceuticals and dressings continued at Park Street. Early days in the Drug Department are recalled by a retired employee who began his apprenticeship at Thackray's at the age of fourteen:

"I joined in 1938 when Harold Platt was Manager, and after a few months' running errands, I was given a job in the lab. It wasn't a lab as such in those days, but where mixtures were dispensed. We used to prepare 20, 40 or even 80 gallons in large barrels stood on the floor. The mixtures were stirred with a big pole, filtered through asbestos and ladled by hand into buckets before being poured through funnels from the top of steps into the barrels. Doctors would order these medicines - cough mixtures, tonics and so on - two or four pints at a time. As they were in concentrated form, say to be diluted one part medicine to seven parts water, doctors didn't have to carry large amounts around with them."

Among Thackray's medicines, which staff could purchase from the retail shop at a discount, was a green cough mixture known as *tussi sed,* today singled out by past employees because of its memorable name. The medicine was actually *Linctus tussi sedativa* which derived its name from the Latin *tussis,* meaning cough, and *sedatus,* meaning calm or quiet. Alongside *tussi sed.* were black *tussi nig(ra)* and red *tussi rub(ra).*

Apart from one or two items, such as aspirins and "Thackray's Pile Pills", most medicines and pills were made up for individual patients from doctors' prescriptions. In pre-war days, pill ingredients would be ground in a pestle and mortar, combined with glucose syrup to achieve a plastic consistency, then pressed into the parallel grooves of a wooden pill-making board. The resultant pills at this stage were square and therefore unsuitable for swallowing until their edges and corners had been smoothed with a boxwood pill rounder; finally, they were varnished or sometimes, for an extra charge, silver-coated.

A visit to the doctor could be expensive in pre-NHS times, so the pharmacist played a much more important role in diagnosis and treatment than his modern counterpart. Often, the customer would take the recommended remedy while still in the shop, sitting on one of two chairs provided. This practice could have its drawbacks. On one occasion, a customer came in complaining of queasiness and was given - reasonably, in the circumstances - a seidlitz powder, a common remedy for indigestion. The customer drank the preparation and promptly keeled over and died. In fact, the man had suffered a heart attack and the pharmacist's action was not to blame.

The retail shop's position on a windy corner formed by the junction of Great George Street and Portland Street gave rise to another service staff were frequently asked to perform: removing grit from eyes. A fine camelhair brush, dipped in Number One Home Office eyedrops - a mixture of cocaine (to act as an anaesthetic) and castor oil - was kept permanently at the ready. No charge was made for the service, but customers were encou-

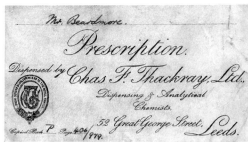

20. **What looks like hieroglyphics to the layman was evidently understood by dispensing pharmacists. This typical prescription, from a doctor in Durban, was given to Sidney Beardmore on one of his visits to South Africa.**

raged to make a donation to the blind, in a collecting box kept in the shop.

Thackray's enjoyed a reputation for being a high-class chemist: "There are things there you can't get anywhere else in Leeds," one apprentice's headmaster had told him when he applied to join the firm. Thackray's maintained its policy of dispensing only private prescriptions, even after the introduction of the National Health Service. But there was no shortage of business: it came from the many nursing homes in the Clarendon Road area of Leeds, from doctors in Park Square and from Leeds City Police, with whom Thackray's had a contract. The Police Surgeon would issue prescriptions, mainly for everyday items like cough mixture and aspirin, the latter often prescribed for the bobby on the beat to counteract the chill experienced after night duty.

The high standard of service that the firm insisted on was maintained by a level of staffing that would be unthinkable today. Under the Manager were an Assistant Manager, two unqualified staff who dealt with the nursing home orders, four apprentices, four errand boys and two cleaners. It was the job of apprentices to dust the mahogany shelves and wipe the shop-rounds. One apprentice, on being asked to dust the section of shelving he had been allocated said, "But I dusted them yesterday." "Yes, and you'll dust them again today," came the reply. The shop was open every day of the year, including Christmas Day. Weekday closing at 7 p.m. (an hour earlier than many other shops in Leeds) meant that apprentices, whose evening classes began at 6.50 p.m. at Leeds Central School, a little further up Great George Street, had to sprint up the road after closing time.

Upstairs from the shop, the huge sterilizer, bought soon after the business began, was still in use. With its boiler situated in the basement, a familiar cry - which must have mystified customers in the shop - could be heard travelling up two floors: "I'm getting steam up!"

The retail shop continued to do good business between the wars, but the main progress of the firm came from its greatly extended distribution and selling force, with the emphasis having shifted from pharmaceuticals and dressings to the surgical business.

CHAPTER 7

The Second World War

The increased space that the acquisition of the Viaduct Road works made available meant that Thackray's could continue its manufacturing expansion. Although exports had become temporarily stagnant, owing to the war, home sales were buoyant.

War inevitably brought a high demand for drugs, dressings and surgical instruments, with injured servicemen returning to Britain for treatment. Among the worst casualties were the burns suffered by airmen shot down in the Battle of Britain. These young men, who included Canadians, Australians, Poles and Czechs, as well as Britons, were later to be thankful that they had been taken to East Grinstead Hospital in Sussex - one of only four plastic surgery units in the country - which was under the direction of the gifted surgeon, Archibald McIndoe. He was Consultant in Plastic Surgery to the Royal Air Force and was later knighted in recognition of his pioneering work.

At East Grinstead, McIndoe wrought miracles of reconstructive surgery, painstakingly rebuilding faces so badly burned that they were unrecognisable. Through this work, McIndoe became a household name. It was Thackray's who made many of the instruments for this delicate surgery, including dissecting forceps and scissors to his own design.

McIndoe had come to Britain from the USA at the suggestion of Lord Moynihan who had been impressed by the young New Zealander's skill in the operating theatre. (Perhaps McIndoe's thick, stubby fingers so deftly used reminded Moynihan of himself when young.) On arriving in this country, however, the job Moynihan had led McIndoe to expect did not materialise. Instead, McIndoe turned to a New Zealand cousin he had never met, Sir Harold Gillies, himself a leading plastic surgeon who had made his name restoring the shattered faces of soldiers returning from the trenches in the First World War.

There were no textbooks to fall back on in those days: the "strange new art" of plastic surgery, as Gillies called it, involved sketches on the backs of envelopes before operations. And that is just how new surgical instruments were designed, too. Gillies had had instruments made for him by Thackray's (many in the catalogue bear his name); as McIndoe had begun his career in Britain acting as "bag carrier" for his eminent cousin and serving what amounted to an apprenticeship with him, it is perhaps not surprising that McIndoe chose the same firm to make instruments for him.

Credit here must go to Edgar Blackburn, Thackray's representative in the south. He was an urbane man, with a fund of knowledge which he knew how to use diplomatically with eminent surgeons, many of whom came from leading centres of plastic surgery in the South East: Queen Mary's at Roehampton, Mount Vernon and East Grinstead. They would discuss their instrument requirements with Blackburn, sometimes involving the minutest variation to existing patterns, so it was essential that he was well informed.

21. Thackray's showroom at Park Street, known as the front shop, where surgeons could call in person to buy instruments.

55

Operating from impressive offices in London's Regent Street, and after the war in Welbeck Street, Blackburn made sure Thackray's served his customers well; he knew how to squeeze extra production out of Leeds, and local subcontractors, when necessary. The fact that McIndoe did not take his business to London firms - which, after all, would have been a more obvious choice for a surgeon based in East Grinstead and, later, in London's Harley Street - is undoubtedly due to Blackburn's efforts and underlines the importance of Thackray's maintaining a London presence: they had to be seen as a national company, not just a provincial one. Maintaining a base in the West End of London and, later, a depot at Stamford Hill (home of Thackray-owned British Cystoscope Co and T. Selby & Co Ltd) was expensive but worthwhile, as the image they created helped to convince people that Thackray's was indeed a national company.

Without the London office, it is unlikely that Thackray's would have been in plastic surgery at all. As well as fostering links with surgeons at the plastic surgery centres in the South East, Blackburn, and his successor, Fred Harrison, won profitable accounts at the major London teaching hospitals. The significance of instrument sales such as these was that orders for other Thackray goods would tend to follow.

One of the craftsmen who worked from surgeons' backs-of-envelopes sketches for instruments was Arthur Hallam. Hallam had joined the firm in the 1914-18 War, making leg irons and splints for casualties. He was an inventive instrument-maker, and had devised many ingenious new designs from surgeons' briefs. In the Second World War Hallam turned his skill to providing the means of survival and escape to servicemen who were to be dropped by parachute across the Channel.

A colleague describes his work: "He fitted folding scissors, saws and wire-cutters into the heels of boots - people would say, 'Oh, Arthur's mending shoes again,' - and he fitted compasses into tunic buttons and Gigli saws [a flexible saw rather like a cheese cutter], into coat collars." Hallam was awarded the OBE in recognition of his unique contribution to the war effort.

An insight into Thackray's war-related activities is provided by the firm's accounts. In 1941 the firm acquired air-raid shelters and covenanted money: in 1942 they gave £50 for seven

56

years to the YMCA War Service Fund and a year later, £105 for seven years to the Merchant Navy. Members of the staff adopted a minesweeper, too; women in the firm knitted socks and scarves for the crew and generally looked after their creature comforts.

After the war, crew members presented the firm with a white ensign - which was later used to decorate the Park Street building for the Queen's Coronation in 1953 - and a barometer with an engraved plaque which hung in the porch of Park Street for years, until it was stolen.

The war years were recalled by Joe Colehan, writing in a company newsletter some years later. Colehan, one of the last of the line of qualified pharmacists taken on by Thackray's, later became Manager of the Raymed Division. He joined the firm, as he said, "the day after war broke out", on Monday, 4th September, 1939.

"We had a ration of honey, sugar and treacle during the war and as part of my 'extra-curricular' training I evolved a formula for boiling these three ingredients, and pouring the mixture into a deep enamelled iron tray; the resultant toffee was well received. However, I had difficulty trying to explain to Mr Platt that this lovely smell was a figment of his imagination!

"Nash's fish shop, the bookies and two snooker tables in St George's Institute were also very handily placed and were often the cause of slow progress back to retail. These particular memories are probably the reason why I have always said to my apprentices, 'It does not matter what you do or where you go, I shall find you because I have done it all myself.'

"Quite a few employees met their future spouses in Park Street and quite a few employees made sure that certain people were not their future spouses at Park Street! Of course, because of the wartime situation there were a lot of call-ups into the forces and lots of visits from servicemen and women on leave. Mercer Gray did his best to claim that the work could be classed as a 'reserved occupation', and he was often successful in obtaining a deferment. Some of the older staff volunteered for the Home Guard and came to work in battledress, whilst others did one night's fire-watching per week for which they were allowed the privilege of sleeping in Mr Tod's office."

At the retail shop, two fire-watchers took turns to sleep on the examination couches in the orthopaedic department. The extra pay for a night of fire-watching was two shillings and the overtime pay at that time for two hours' work was one shilling tea money.

The extra shilling was something staff remember well: "You could buy five Woodbines and a sandwich and a pot of tea for sixpence. Then you could go to the cinema with the sixpence you had left. We used to be paid ten shillings a week until the age of sixteen, starting work at 8.30 and finishing at six in the evening, with one-and-a-half hours for lunch. People used to go home for lunch, by bus or tram, but you could travel a long way in those days in fifteen minutes."

Others could buy their lunch at a British Restaurant, a feature of wartime Britain where hot meals were provided cheaply by the local authority on a non-profit-making basis and where, incidentally, the labour-saving system of self-service originated. Young apprentices working at Viaduct Road could buy a loaf of bread for their lunch which they would dip into a penny bowl of hot soup from the British Restaurant on Kirkstall Road, leaving them enough money to buy cigarettes, too.

22. Noel Thackray (right) on a trip to the United States in the 1940s. (The Packard belonged to his American hosts.)

The war brought a big influx of women into the firm, to train for jobs that men had had to leave for service duties. Jack Ridsdale, who had joined Thackray's as a fourteen-year-old apprentice just before the war, and was then working as a fitter, said that each person in the department was asked to train a woman assistant. After the war, he says, he continued to train apprentices. His natural ability in this field made him the obvious choice for supervising apprentices' training at Thackray's.

The foundations of training laid by Jack Ridsdale later grew into an Apprentices School, created in 1961 out of the difficulty in recruiting suitably qualified labour, especially in connection with the manufacture of surgical instruments which was more of a craft than light engineering. Latterly, sixteen-year-old school-leavers served a four-year apprenticeship, of which the first year was spent at an Engineering Industrial Training Board college and the remaining three completing work experience at Thackray's.

During the war and even into the 1950s, hand work represented a large proportion of Park Street's activities. Some of the young female employees did a range of jobs, including sewing yellow burns dressings on to bandages. One recalls: "We also used to roll up catgut [for sutures] and put it in envelopes, so many to a box, for which we were paid extra. My least favourite job was in repairs. Broken glass syringes came in, sometimes still with blood on, and we had to knock off the broken glass with toffee hammers."

Another who was working at Park Street from the end of the war recalls dyeing silkworm gut from Spain - different colours representing different rates of absorption into the body - which were then left on the windowsill to dry before being sterilized. Her other duties included plaiting horsetail hair in groups of a hundred and making bandages from a large piece of lint, cut into strips on a wooden frame and rolled individually by hand. A colleague's job was to inject iodine into glass ampoules with a syringe and seal them with a Bunsen burner flame.

Today, it seems surprising that even as late as the 1950s so many jobs were carried out by hand, but the business - in common with the rest of the trade - had been traditionally craft-oriented; it was not until the 1960s that this labour-intensive approach was gradually modified in favour of more highly mechanised production.

CHAPTER 8

The Post-War Years

The closing years of the war saw the development of revolutionary antibiotics, which were radically to change the treatment of a host of illnesses. Thackray's was awarded the important new distributorship of one of these, Sulphadiazine, developed by the pharmaceutical firm, May & Baker (M & B).

Vaccines, too, were undergoing major advances. Soon after the war, Thackray's carried stocks of Lederle's Immune Serum Gamma Globulin, a new measles vaccine with approximately four times the potency of its predecessor. Such agencies were highly profitable: turnover for the Lederle account in 1946, for instance, was almost equal to the firm's total exports.

The company's ability to anticipate and to respond to changing circumstances contributed greatly to its success. For instance, in 1947, when coal was nationalised, representatives were encouraged to make calls to collieries to inform their medical officers of Thackray's ability to supply their ambulance rooms with drugs and equipment. The same year, reps were instructed to provide catalogues and estimates to City and County Health Departments in preparation for the completion of health centres under the new Health Act which was to come into force the following year.

Indeed, the introduction of the National Health Service in 1948 was the most important single factor to affect Thackray's after the war. The Ministry of Health took over all voluntary and municipal hospitals, and the extensive re-equipping that followed led to a busy and expansive period for all sections of the business. (The Leeds Postmaster remarked to Mercer Gray at this time that Thackray's generated one of the biggest, if not the biggest, parcel posts in the city.)

Service has been described as the lodestone of Thackray's. The firm had already established a depot to facilitate distribution in the South of England; now they needed another, to the North, to supply Scottish customers promptly, and Glasgow was chosen for a second warehouse. At this time, too, a South African

60

23. The Christmas dinner-dance continued to be the highlight of the firm's social calendar until the 1970s, when staff numbers had increased to the point where no single venue could accommodate everybody. Here, at the Capitol in the early Fifties, are (from left to right), standing: Mercer Gray, Mrs Douglas Thackray, Dr Douglas Thackray, Edgar Blackburn; seated, far side: Richard Wainwright, Joyce Wainwright, Mrs Mercer Gray, Mrs Charles Thackray; seated, near side: Roland and Freda Davy (Chas F.'s daughter) with their daughter, Helen, between them.

subsidiary was created, initially based in Cape Town. As a prosperous dominion, South Africa offered a potentially lucrative market with the additional advantage that unlike Canada, for instance, it had no major UK competitors.

The finances of the South African operation were overseen by Scurrah Wainwright's son, Richard - like his father, a chartered accountant with Beevers & Adgie. In its early years, post war, the South African subsidiary was substantially profitable owing to valuable distributorships - for example, Davis & Geck sutures - and to the emphasis on quality at South Africa's leading hospitals, most of which had strong UK links. Eventually, however, the distributorships were superseded by European manufacturers sending machine-made stampings for hand-finishing locally and then selling direct; hospitals moved their instrument purchasing on to a tendering basis on which Thackray prices lost the market. A policy leading to closure was adopted, which meant that substantial stocks of instruments were returned to the UK. By the final stages, Cape Town and Johannesburg were able to repay the whole of their debt to the parent company, leaving a profit on share capital.

Exports, slowed for the war years, began again in earnest immediately hostilities ended. Yearly total export turnover, averaging about £50,000 during the war years, leapt to £120,000 in 1946 and continued to rise in the 1950s. By this time, Thackray's catalogues amounted to two hefty tomes. An identical, but miniaturised, version was therefore produced for overseas use. Delivery costs could be kept to a minimum and it could fit more easily into sometimes cramped quarters in Africa and Asia.

Thackray's sales force was once more increased, with some representatives travelling overseas full time. The life of the overseas rep. was not always as glamorous as some of the exotic destinations might suggest. Bill Piggin, who was taken on by

24. Medical exhibitions, such as this one in Glasgow in 1948, gave Thackray's a valuable "shop window" for surgeons.

Charles Thackray as a qualified pharmacist in 1930, and was Export Director of the company from 1957 until his retirement in 1976, recalled:

"When visiting African countries we had to stay in guest houses. These had been well run in British times, but the accommodation had deteriorated. On one occasion, in Sierra Leone, the booking clerk told me I would have to share a room. I not only shared a room, but a bed! The other chap was an agronomist with an American company who wanted to talk all night. Another time, in Nigeria, I shared a room with five other people and woke in the morning to find vultures outside the window."

It could be a dangerous business, too: one overseas representative contracted cerebral malaria in Africa, another tells of a narrow escape when caught in crossfire in Venezuela.

A less hazardous way of promoting Thackray's products was participation in international trade fairs. Frequently, orders for equipment would be taken at the exhibition stand but, as Bill Piggin pointed out, "Sometimes the trade exhibitions weren't so much of benefit from a commercial point of view, as to show the flag; they were subsidised by the government." One such involved an invitation to Hungary a year or so after the revolution of 1957.

"We were invited to go to Budapest. Two left-wing Members of Parliament, Ian Mikardo and Jo Richardson, had formed a company and got a group together. At the last minute somebody dropped out, so at very short notice Ian Mikardo rang me and asked us to go. He also asked me if I could bring out his dinner jacket as, ironically for a Communist country, the Hungarians were laying on a do for which we had to wear evening dress."

However well planned, overseas exhibitions ran the inherent risk of transport problems. One such involved the shipment of exhibits to Mombasa, Kenya, which were then to continue inland by rail to Uganda's capital, Kampala. Stands were built, Thackray personnel were ready, but there were no exhibits. The train carrying Thackray's goods had been derailed. Eventually the shipment arrived, in pouring rain, and operating tables were carried on shoulders across a sea of mud into the exhibition marquee.

The Second Generation

The 1950s saw the second generation of the three families assume new responsibilities. In 1956 Mercer Gray died, and was succeeded as Managing Director, jointly, by Charles Thackray's sons, Noel and Tod, who had been Directors of the company since 1934.

Noel, urbane and dapper, more often than not to be seen about town wearing a dinner jacket and white silk scarf, was known in the drawing-rooms of Leeds' leading families. He was an attractive character: although not especially good-looking, his undisputed charm earned him a reputation for being something of a ladies' man. He clearly enjoyed socialising - and was good at it, at ease whether chatting at parties, where he was likely to dance every dance, or with customers. His social success did not, however, extend to his closest relationships and in the opinion of his son, Paul, this led to two unfortunate marriages.

For all his ability in business, Noel never gained any professional qualification, though he worked slavishly, even obsessively, at the firm, and could barely tear himself away to go on holiday. He found it difficult to delegate and even when he became Managing Director, he insisted on seeing every order that came into Park Street himself. Noel was constantly rushing about (it has even been said that he always looked as if he were about to start a race) but he still had time for people and he was well liked and respected in the firm. Two bouts of rheumatic fever as a child had made him short of breath, but that didn't stop him chain-smoking. And when his doctor told him to give up cigarettes, or at least to smoke cigars instead, he followed the advice but chain-smoked the cigars and inhaled the smoke, too.

Noel's younger brother, Tod, was much more retiring by nature. He shared Noel's obsessive streak, a characteristic the two boys seem to have inherited from their father. Unlike Noel, though, Tod learnt to delegate and to pace himself at work. All three Thackray boys (including the youngest, Douglas) were sent to Giggleswick School in North Yorkshire, but Tod's memories of it were so unhappy that he was reluctant ever even to mention the place afterwards. Perhaps he was sensitive to the fact that their father allegedly visited the school only once during their entire school careers.

25. Left to right: Noel Thackray, Mercer Gray, Scurrah Wainwright, Tod Thackray. Brothers Noel and Tod were contrasting characters who brought complementary qualities to the firm.

Tod went on to serve his apprenticeship in pharmacy at Thackray's retail shop in Great George Street and to study at Leeds and Bradford Technical Colleges for his MPS (Membership of the Pharmaceutical Society), as his father had done before him. There appears to have been no parental pressure on Noel to do so. Despite his apparent shyness, Tod was always keen to go out to hospitals to demonstrate new products or to help plan theatre equipment. In fact, he got out and about much more than Noel, who tended to build his rapport with customers on the telephone.

Tod and his wife, Betty, chose to live in a village near Knaresborough, quite a long distance to commute to Leeds by car. Their decision caused a few raised eyebrows in the boardroom, with some wondering how committed Tod could be to the firm. Back in the 1950s, though, no consideration was given to directors' thinking time on their journey to work, for instance. Tod's thoughts evidently did stray from his driving from time to time, as his car was often to be seen with minor scrapes and dents in the bodywork. The vehicle was the source of some amusement at Thackray's; Tod would sometimes have the damage repaired by the firm, but the heavy grade steel used in the manufacture of hospital furniture, welded on to the rather lighter bodywork of the car, meant that the vehicle grew heavier with every repair.

In January 1957, a year after Noel and Tod took up their joint Managing Directorship, Richard Wainwright and Robert Gray - who also later took on the role of Company Secretary in 1976 - were elected to the Board. Richard had inherited his father's business acumen, but was a more genial and approachable figure than the formidable Scurrah, who had the qualities more typical of an earlier generation brought up in Queen Victoria's reign.

In his capacity as financial Director, Richard Wainwright was responsible for preparing Thackray's annual accounts and dealing with the company's tax liabilities.

A family firm, such as Thackray's, presents special problems regarding its future financial security when the share ownership is divided among the families involved. Concerned that a high rate of death duties should not drain away the company's resources, nor upset the ownership structure of the four distinct families, Richard Wainwright advised the heads of family, each with large Thackray shareholdings, to establish family trusts by making over some of their shares to trustees for the benefit of their children; and in respect of shares each director retained, the company insured their lives to the extent required to meet likely tax liabilities on death.

On this basis, the company weathered, without difficulty, the financial consequences of the deaths of Mercer Gray and, later, Scurrah Wainwright and Noel Thackray. Though commonplace nowadays, such arrangements were then quite innovative and meant that Thackray's avoided the pitfall that other family firms experienced in the 1950s and 60s, when high death duties forced them into a sale.

Richard Wainwright was also instrumental in instigating a fundamental change in the way the company was financed. Historically, directors had lent to the company all their unused remuneration and had drawn only modest salaries and extremely modest dividends. Wainwright convinced the board that it would be more appropriate to turn to the company's bank for working capital and to repay Directors all or, if they wished, most of their loans. Directors were thus able to spread less narrowly the investment of their personal savings, and the company came under the discipline of having systematically to present a convincing case to the bank. The modest dividend policy continued, for death duty purposes.

Richard had continued his father's pattern of calling most days to talk to the Managing Director and others to discuss whatever was topical. This became impracticable, however, when he was elected to Parliament in 1966, as Liberal member for Colne Valley, whereupon the Park Street visits were reduced to Mondays and Fridays.

Soon after his election to Parliament, he was appointed Liberal Spokesman on Economic Affairs, a position he held throughout his parliamentary career, from 1966-70 and from 1974-87. His detailed knowledge of the country's economy was a valuable asset to Thackray's Board, and by the same token his practical business experience lent weight to his political pronouncements.

Fellow director Robert Gray took charge of the company's confidential records - directors' bonuses, pension arrangements and so on - and had responsibility for personnel matters. He was well suited to this role, having been brought up with the business, so to speak, which meant that he was known to everyone in the firm and, in turn, he knew all Thackray's employees personally.

One aspect of his job was overseeing and keeping in touch with the company's growing number of pensioners, who got together annually at the firm's Christmas lunch. For many years, Joe Colehan, at the piano, used to lead the pensioners in a lively sing-song, but after he died in 1986, children from local schools entertained the guests with a carol concert. Food for the pensioners' lunch was organised by Robert Gray's daughter, Janet Fairfoot, a qualified caterer who had supervised the canteen at Park Street since it was introduced in 1976. Robert Gray's son, Michael, also worked for the firm and was to take over his father's role as Company Secretary in 1984.

Fifties and Sixties prosperity

In the climate of post-war prosperity, manufacturing continued to increase. Thackray's once again outgrew its premises and, unable to expand the Viaduct Road site, the company looked elsewhere. A factory at St Anthony's Road, Beeston, in South Leeds, was up for sale. Although it had more space than required at the time, Tod Thackray was convinced that the company should buy the site and overcame his natural diffidence to press forcefully for the purchase and persuade fellow directors to go ahead. As a result, the Beeston site was acquired in 1957 at a cost of £55,000 (equivalent to just over £600,000 today). It has proved to have been a shrewd investment in the light of subsequent expansion.

Manufacturing and drugs moved to Beeston and the now-empty Viaduct Road building was put up for sale. It failed to attract a buyer, however, owing to a proposed plan to straighten a dog-leg bend in the road adjoining the factory (a plan which was never carried out). In the event, therefore, the Drug Department, together with Wholesale Pharmacy, took over the premises. (The removal of the instrument works from Viaduct Road was not without drama. A young man who had been employed at the works, "a right nice lad", according to workmates, had been convicted of murder in 1945, a *crime passionel*

26. The Beeston factory. This aerial view bears out Tod Thackray's argument in 1957 that the site should be bought because it lent itself to expansion. Later, Thackray's built a new warehouse on the land at the top of the picture, having exchanged it with Leeds City Council for a piece they owned on the extreme right.

it seems. The bloodstained clothing of the victim could not be found at the time of his trial, but was discovered, twelve years later, hidden under machinery when the works were transferred to Beeston.)

The Beeston factory had belonged to a screw manufacturer since it was built in the First World War. "The first thing we had to do," remembers Robert Gray, "was to scrape up tons of grease off the floor. We did a lot of the work ourselves. I remember Tod Thackray with his shirtsleeves rolled up, pulling out old wiring and scraping the floors."

Tod moved his office from Viaduct Road to Beeston, where he set about equipping the building for the manufacture of surgical instruments and hospital furniture.

Thackray's expansion in Leeds was followed by the acquisition of two specialist manufacturing companies, the British Cystoscope Co. Ltd, in Clerkenwell, London, and Thomas Rudd Ltd of Sheffield, makers of surgical scissors. What both of these

27. One of the largest steam-heated sterilizers made (this one was designed for sterilization of hay in veterinary research, but it had other disinfectant uses). The apparatus was given scale for the catalogue photograph by one of Thackray's staff - though it should be admitted that the shortest man in the works was chosen.

69

companies had in common was a highly skilled work-force producing instruments to the exacting standards expected of Thackray products.

The purchase of these two firms was largely the work of Sidney Beardmore, who had been one of Thackray's first over-seas representatives, following in Noel Farley's footsteps in the Twenties and Thirties as a personable and thoroughly equipped representative.

Beardmore continued to gain agencies for Thackray's, as Farley had done - in particular the profitable Schacht colostomy range from America. He was also responsible for developing the firm's own specialist products with a talent, recall fellow direc-tors, for knowing what could become standard lines. Through his colleague Fred Harrison's contacts with surgeons in the South East, Beardmore developed another top seller for Thackray's in the Leatham stethoscope, second only to Charnley products (whose importance we shall see in the following chapter) and the Schacht range in terms of sales. His flair for product literature and his good relationships with surgeons helped to extend Thackray's product range in orthopaedics, plastic surgery and ostomy, to the extent that, in the opinion of John and Paul Thackray, Managing Director and Deputy Man-aging Director respectively from 1978 to 1990, many of the company's existing products have been built on foundations laid by Beardmore.

Although most sections of Thackray's business had been expanding since the end of the war, changes in the pattern of medical practice brought about by the introduction of the National Health Service had led to a decline in business at the retail shop in Great George Street. Prescriptions from nursing homes and physicians with practices in Park Square, on which the trade of the shop had depended in the past, had declined since 1948; at the same time, profit margins on products had dwindled so that, with the majority of customers being medical or staff entitled to a 10 percent discount, the shop was not even covering its overheads. Consequently, even with the excellent Joe Colehan as manager, the shop became unprofitable.

Joe (brother of TV producer Barney Colehan, who was well known for his creation of the Leeds City Varieties Music Hall programme, *The Good Old Days*) was a popular figure and he had

29. Joe Colehan, last manager of the retail shop, just before the premises closed for good in 1962. The mahogany shelving and shop-rounds had hardly altered since the shop first opened for business sixty years earlier.

© Yorkshire Post Newspapers.

made many friends among his customers. They packed the shop, particularly at Christmas time when, as one Thackray staff member put it, "Consultants' wives could be seen buying expensive perfumes on their husbands' accounts" and Thackray's staff could buy gifts from a display arranged in a room behind the shop.

Despite the popularity of the shop amongst its regular customers, the balance sheet could not be ignored and the decision was taken to close it in January 1962, sixty years after Thackray and Wainwright had started their business there and a century since it had begun as a pharmacy under Samuel Taylor's ownership.

In general, however, the post-war reconstruction period of the 1950s and 60s was highly profitable for the medical business, with large sums of public money directed towards new hospitals and universities.

In 1961, for the first time since the National Health Service came into being, Regional Hospital Boards were encouraged by the Minister of Health to make long-term plans for hospital building, with an allocation of more than £60 million capital expenditure for 1961-3 and further sums forthcoming by the middle of the decade. This new attitude towards public health spending virtually guaranteed Thackray's a fast-expanding home market for the Sixties (with the advantage that individual Hospital Board buying would be more evenly spread over the financial year), and made a sound base for increasing export trade.

The 1960s were notable, too, for the important association Thackray's was to develop with the orthopaedic surgeon, Sir John Charnley. Knighted for his work in the field of total hip replacement, Charnley played a significant role in the company's fortunes and development.

CHAPTER 9

The Charnley Era

The links Thackray's had formed with the Leeds General Infirmary in the early days of the business had been strengthened by further generations of surgeons who succeeded Moynihan and his colleagues. Indeed, the numerous instruments listed in the firm's catalogue that are named after the surgeon who devised them, bear witness to the close ties that remained between Thackray's and the medical profession.

One such link, in 1947, was with Mr R. Broomhead, a Leeds orthopaedic surgeon. Keen to improve his instrumentation, Broomhead asked an engineering friend of his, Edgar Alcock, to help him with technical aspects of design and to produce accurate scale drawings which Thackray's could work from. The arrangement worked well and Broomhead's retractors can still be seen in the firm's catalogue.

Another orthopaedic surgeon who approached Thackray's in a similar vein, and whose name was to become as famous as Moynihan's and McIndoe's, was John Charnley, who had a remarkable relationship with Thackray's spanning more than thirty years. Charnley's first known contact with the firm dates back to about 1947, when the instrument curator at the Manchester Royal Infirmary, where Charnley was an orthopaedic surgeon, recommended Thackray's as an alternative to a long-established London company who had been making instruments for Charnley. For Thackray's to be chosen instead represented an important challenge.

The first instruments Thackray's made specially for Charnley are thought to have been dissecting forceps. He then asked the firm to make instruments associated with his method of pinning fractures of the femur (thigh bone) with a screw and plate. Charnley worked closely with the foreman in the development workshop, Arthur Hallam, for whom the surgeon developed great respect. Thackray's also manufactured an orthopaedic table to Charnley's design. First developed in 1951, it continued to be manufactured until 1986.

29. Sir John Charnley, the remarkable orthopaedic surgeon whose association with Thackray's was the key to developing the hip replacement operation.

However, the surgeon's most notable collaboration with Thackray's concerned total hip replacement, an operation to reduce pain and restore movement to the hip by implanting a manmade replacement for the deteriorated ball-and-socket joint. The artificial hip (or prosthesis) comprised a ball-ended stem which fitted into the patient's thigh bone and a cup which took the place of the socket (or acetabulum) in the pelvis. Charnley developed and refined his hip replacement operation throughout his long association with Thackray's and was still making improvements when he died after a heart attack in 1982 at the age of seventy.

The close collaboration between surgeon and manufacturer is revealed in Charnley's copious correspondence with the firm. Sometimes he would write three or four letters in a week, concerning himself with everything from the minutiae of design to broader, commercial issues. He was without question a perfectionist and, to achieve the standards he insisted on, could be forthright in his criticism of Thackray's when he felt it necessary; but he was quick to apologise, too. Thackray's, though tolerant of his demands, could reply with equal vigour and an understanding grew between them.

Development of the hip replacement operation began soon after the Second World War. At the forefront was the pioneering surgeon G.K. McKee of Norwich. He was using a stainless steel replacement joint, but in the late 1950s it was realised that a high rate of failure was due to the loosening of components. It became clear that some sort of bone cement was likely to be the answer. Charnley began using a dental acrylic cement to wedge the artificial thigh bone, or stem, in place. The advantage of grouting in this way was that the load (the patient's body weight) was distributed equally, whereas the uncemented variety used previously tended to create a few pressure points.

Free, and therefore painless, movement of the joint was the objective and to this end Charnley looked for two surfaces which would need no artificial lubrication. He found the substance he was looking for, not unlike bone cartilage ("gristle") in appearance, in Teflon®, the material used to line non-stick cooking pans.

In these pioneering days of the operation, Thackray's made the stainless steel stem, while Charnley made the Teflon sockets himself, turning them on a lathe in his workshop at home. According to Charnley's biographer, Professor William Waugh, Wednesdays became "socket nights" at the Charnley home, in readiness for his operating list on Thursdays at the Wrightington Hospital near Wigan, where he was Consultant Orthopaedic Surgeon. This arrangement continued until 1963, when Thackray's took over production of the sockets.

Charnley had bought his lathe in 1946 (it is now displayed at the Thackray Medical Museum in Leeds). He had had no formal training as an engineer, but he was a dextrous craftsman and had a natural flair for mechanics. He closely supervised his technicians at the workshop he had created in the 1950s at Wrightington, getting them to produce instruments and modifying them himself before asking Thackray's to manufacture them. As time went on, Thackray's contributed their own design suggestions, and this continual exchange of ideas between the firm and surgeons at Wrightington was a significant factor in the advance of the hip operation.

In 1961, a grant from Manchester Regional Hospital Board enabled Charnley to build a biomechanical workshop and laboratory at Wrightington, and the title "Centre for Hip Surgery, Wrightington Hospital" was officially adopted.

Funding was a constant source of concern to Charnley. In 1966 he came to an agreement with Thackray's that in consideration of "waiving his right to royalties on the sale of prostheses bearing his name", they would pay his research fund £1 for every prosthesis sold. Later, the arrangement was modified to include a payment on the royalties of Charnley patented instruments. In 1970, Thackray's also undertook to pay the salaries of two skilled technicians at Wrightington, who clearly deserved a higher rate than their NHS classification as "orthopaedic appliance makers" could command. It is worth mentioning here that despite the huge success of Charnley's hip replacement operation, he did not become a rich man, preferring to plough the proceeds of his success into his research fund.

By 1962 it became evident that Teflon® was not the ideal material for socket replacement because particles wore off and caused discomfort in patients. Impressed by laboratory wear test results of a new material, a high molecular weight polyethylene, Charnley implanted a sample in his own thigh to ensure that there would be no adverse tissue reactions as there had been with Teflon. With no reaction discernible after six months, Charnley began implanting the new material into patients.

However, he wanted to avoid other surgeons taking up his operation before the new material had been proven and consequently he placed an embargo on the sale of implants "for some future period as yet undefined".

By 1968, even after five years' experience with the new material, he allowed Thackray's to sell only to those surgeons whom he had personally approved, although the special instruments were available, as they could be used for other hip operations. Such a restriction often put Thackray's in the embarrassing position of having to refuse requests from eminent surgeons for Charnley implants.

Replying to a surgeon in Harrogate who had been able to purchase instruments but not prostheses from Thackray's, Charnley made his views clear in a letter dated January 1968:

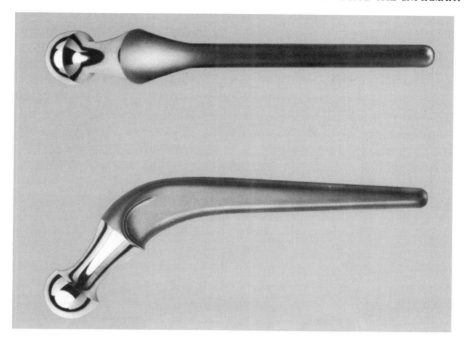

30. A stainless steel hip. A range of sizes was available "off the shelf" to suit different patients.

"I am worried about unleashing a large number of total prosthetic replacements using plastic sockets before a full assessment of the five year results is available.

"The restriction applies solely to the sale of the prosthetic implant (i.e. the femoral head and the plastic socket). It does not apply to the availability of the full armamentarium [set of instruments] for inserting these implants, using the lateral route ... This distinction has been made because the instruments can be used with other types of implant than my own ...

"In order to qualify for permission ... I am stipulating that surgeons must visit Wrightington for a minimum period of two days ... I hope this explains the apparent inconsistency of being able to purchase the instruments with which to do the operation with a restriction on obtaining the implants to be used with it.

"One of my main worries is that surgeons will do this operation through exposures which avoid raising the great

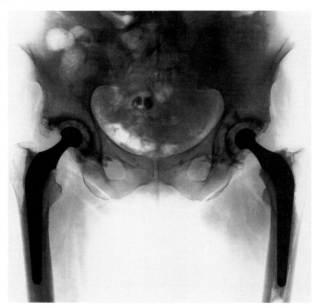

31. Radiograph of a replacement hip. The stainless steel stem has been inserted into the patient's thigh bone, replacing the part that has deteriorated. The pelvis has been fitted with a plastic socket, made visible on the X-ray by a steel wire.

Courtesy Mr J.O. Lawton, MA, FRCS.

trochanter [the bony knob at the top of the thigh bone]. I am very frightened that if they do this they will find that this prosthesis might dislocate and they will therefore blame the prosthesis."

Charnley's caution in making the implants generally available did not prevent considerable demand for the product, however, and in April 1968, writing to Sidney Beardmore, the director responsible for instrument and implant sales, Charnley berates the company for not manufacturing in sufficient quantity. He ends his letter with a request for a meeting with Tod Thackray and Beardmore, a not uncommon occurrence as he always demanded attention from the highest level. (One Thackray director recalls that at one time no fewer than four directors were involved with Charnley's criticisms, or as the surgeon himself put it in another letter to Beardmore: "I hope you do not consider my criticisms of the products ... as 'complaints'. They are of course constructive criticisms for the improvement of the product and I feel sure you welcome these and know that they are not just 'bellyaches'.")

Thackray's responded to Charnley's chiding by improving their manufacturing capability and by the end of 1968, Beardmore could write to Charnley: "As from January 1st next, we shall increase our rate of production of prostheses by 25% and our anticipated production will be 6,000 per annum, which could be increased to 7,000 by the end of the year. Additional production to 10,000 per annum could be organised without too much difficulty."

Thackray's instrument manager at this time recalled that such was the demand for Charnley implants and instruments that he was forced to have a lockable cage constructed at Beeston to stop other departments, such as Exports, plundering the limited stock.

The mechanics of the hip replacement operation had become established in the 1950s and 60s, but recovery in some patients was hampered by infection in the wound. In a letter to Thackray's dated January 1968, Charnley wrote:

"One of my technicians was telling me about your ideas of trying to avoid dust in the area where you are finishing the prostheses and I think this is an extremely important thing. Ideally a completely sealed room should be used with filtered air blowing in to get dust-free conditions. This is not an extremely expensive installation, but I think it would pay off in the end. The plastic sockets should also be done in this atmosphere."

Thackray's created a model "clean" area for the packing of prostheses which were sterilized and individually packed. In due course, tailor-made blister packing was provided by a Thackray subsidiary, Tweedbank Surgical, in Scotland, who were involved in the manufacture of steel instruments and implants. Thackray's became leaders in the field of sterile packing, not simply meeting British Standard requirements but setting them. Both the British Standards Institute and its international equivalent, the ISO, have liaised with Thackray's staff in the development of sterile environments and wear testing.

In due course, Charnley stopped making a personal selection of surgeons and any who had spent the two days at Wrightington could buy his prosthesis. By the early 1970s, the product was

79

made generally available and Thackray's were fully stretched to produce the quantity of Charnley hips and instruments required by orthopaedic surgeons.

It was at this time that Noel Thackray died. The consequences of Noel's death are described in more detail later but, in essence, it led to a reorganisation of the firm's management. Tod Thackray took over his brother's role as Chairman and became sole Managing Director, Tod's son John became Deputy Managing Director and his nephew (Noel's son, Paul) was appointed Director responsible for Interplan Hospital Projects and much of the company's purchasing activity.

The changes coincided with a period when government was encouraging industry and universities to collaborate in order to make full use of the most up-to-date techniques available - an era associated with the "white heat of technology", when a Labour government appointed MP Tony Benn the first Minister of Technology.

In this context, Thackray's approached Leeds Polytechnic Industrial Liaison Unit for advice on how to meet their increasing production demands. As a result, Jim Boyd, an engineer

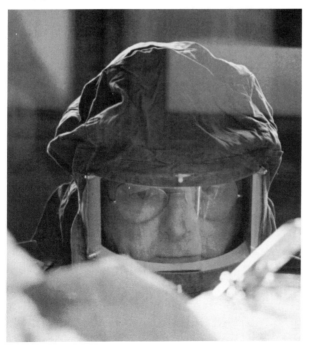

32. Charnley, seen through the visor of the all-enveloping "body exhaust" helmet and gown he pioneered. The risk of bacterial infection originating from the surgeon was reduced to a minimum by a process of continuously sucking air from the gown during operations.

who had been with one of the largest electronic components companies in Europe, was appointed General Works Manager in March 1971, and shortly afterwards Ron Frank, who, as lecturer in management studies had produced the works organisation report commissioned by Thackray's, joined the firm as Group Management Accountant and Corporate Planning Manager.

Jim Boyd and Ron Frank were the firm's first professionally trained managers from non-medical industry. At the time they joined, Thackray's themselves were producing only about 25 percent of their total sales, compared to about 75 percent in 1990. Manufacturing was craft-oriented, employing highly skilled men who could turn out excellent products. However, such craftsmanship had two inherent drawbacks: there were difficulties in achieving sufficient consistency in the tight tolerances required and there was little flexibility of volume.

What was needed was a semi-automated method of production that would not only ensure precision consistency but also allow quick training so that extra shifts could be worked to make up stocks when necessary. Hand work continued to be an important feature of production at Thackray's, but it gradually diminished as a percentage of the total.

"At the time Ron Frank and I joined," Jim Boyd says, "Charnley had just started to take off, and the company wasn't ready. It was like suddenly finding you had the crown jewels of the orthopaedic world, but none of the fundamentals."

The 1970s saw major capital expenditure in machinery which ensured the consistency of production and flexibility of volume that was needed. Computer-controlled machines, each operated by only one technician, could turn out large numbers of stems (50,000 a year in 1990), and a sophisticated electro-chemical process honed the metal to a high degree of accuracy.

By far the biggest expenditure, however, was in equipment for "cold-forming" steel. Femoral stems had been made from stainless steel from the outset, but it was lower in bending strength than other metals, so Jim Boyd asked Thackray's metallurgist to investigate the possibility of improving its mechanical characteristics. He showed that "cold-forming" - a process whereby steel is compressed between dies at much lower temperatures than conventional forging - could increase the strength of stems by as much as eight times without enlarging them.

In January 1979, Charnley was able to see the new process for himself at Beeston, and wrote after his visit: "I am extremely pleased to see the first products of the cold forming of the stems with little more than linishing [a mechanical smoothing process] and polishing after pressing."

In the continuous effort to find stronger materials, Thackray's carried out tests on a high-nitrogen steel used in North Sea oil rigs called Rex 734®, to discover whether cold forming would improve its fatigue resistance. Out of this research was born Ortron 90®, the culmination of an improved material and cold forming. The new steel was given this unequivocal reference by Charnley in a letter to Thackray's in September, 1980:

"The outstanding cases of [two patients] have both been followed for over two years, are both bilateral operations, are both very vigorous and relatively young men (50 and 46 years), both are heavy patients (246 and 210 lbs), both are over six foot tall, and both are utterly perfect results ..."

The new material, together with design changes resulting from stem-fatigue tests by Thackray's research laboratory, was calculated to prolong the life of the implant. There should be no need for another operation during the lifetime of the patient.

Charnley's enthusiasm for the new design is apparent in this letter to Tod Thackray, written in June 1982 shortly before he died:

"I enclose two X-rays, one of the conventional prosthesis as we have made it for over twenty years and one representing the two specimens of the new narrow neck which I have introduced in patients clinically.

"I think you will agree that the narrow neck is very elegant and that it makes the original prosthesis look very clumsy. I am therefore writing to urge you to consider very seriously putting this 10mm narrow neck on the market as soon as possible. However, a very very important detail in publicity is that if we are as confident in the new steel as indeed we are ... then it is a sign of absolute confidence in the new metal to reduce the diameter."

It is characteristic of Charnley to mention Thackray's publicity material. He played an active part in preparing the entries of his products in the firm's catalogue, writing descriptions of his own designs himself, or sometimes amending what Thackray's had drafted. "I have been thinking about this catalogue ..." he wrote in a letter to Tod dated June 1982, "and it is my feeling that the line drawings are now very old-fashioned and not very glamorous. On the other hand there are some splendid instruments made by Thackray's which would be much better shown by half-tone blocks." Tod was responsible for compiling the last full Charnley catalogue, with notes written by the surgeon himself.

Demand for Charnley products was high and took the company into new export fields. In theory, the United States offered a vast potential market - the Charnley name had been patented in the US in 1969 - but there were major hurdles.

American surgeons were reluctant to be wooed away from the chrome-cobalt implants with which they had become familiar and which they trusted, especially when stainless steel as a material for implants was becoming the subject of scare stories in the States. Additionally, the Thackray name was relatively unknown on the other side of the Atlantic, so products did not have the automatic credibility they enjoyed back home.

It would be unreasonable, too, to expect Thackray's handful of representatives to compete with the hundreds employed by US manufacturers. Successful penetration into the US market would have required the sort of marketing that was unheard of in the UK at that time; American hospitals, for example, expected consignment stocks (not paid for until used) and free sets of instruments.

The massive product liability involved, requiring huge insurance premiums, made Thackray's wary of the American market, too. Competitors' profits were large enough to take account of any possible litigation.

From Charnley's point of view, the question of releasing his product in the USA depended on Thackray's ability to produce the implants in the numbers that would be required. Writing to the company in October 1970, he says: "If under cover of restriction to authorised users you are still not able to supply off the shelf, then I think you would be very foolish to open yourself to general supply, and so starve the authorised users and finally make them break with you for ever ... Quite clearly they will go to [a rival company] rather than wait loyally for Thackray's product."

A year later, another American company was sufficiently worried by the potential of Charnley products in the USA to attempt a smear campaign. They tried to discredit the suitability of stainless steel and the quality of the sockets, putting it about that some were made from material which was "merely standard polyethylene used to make milk bottles, toys and the like". Thackray's had the additional problem of US companies copying their designs, "riding roughshod over your patents", as Charnley put it. In order to satisfy the demands of the US market, in 1974 Thackray granted an American company an option to manufacture Charnley hip prostheses and sockets.

The same year came the threat of legal action from a patient in Los Angeles following the fracture of a femoral stem. It transpired that an ordinary straight narrow stem had been implanted in a patient weighing 300 lb (more than 21 stone). "No wonder it broke," commented Tod Thackray to Charnley. A thick-stemmed prosthesis should have been used. Fortunately, the case never came to court. "It was an irony of fate," commented Charnley at the time, "that the fracture of the prosthesis in a heavy patient indicates that the result of the operation was practically 100%, because a poor result, with a load-sparing limp, is unlikely to result in a fatigue fracture."

Charnley's skill in the operating theatre was undeniable but not in itself unique. What makes his contribution to orthopaedics so remarkable was the combination of this skill with his gift for innovation and the will - including, as he admitted, acting as the "scourge and flail of Thackray's" - to see it through. His contribution to orthopaedic surgery was given due recognition in the citation that accompanied the honorary Doctorate of Laws awarded to Tod Thackray by the University of Leeds in May, 1988:

"He and his company have contributed to some of the greatest advances in orthopaedic surgery this century. Through his long co-operation and friendship with the late Sir John Charnley, Mr Thackray and his company confronted and overcame some of the major problems in orthopaedics. The first great advance was compression arthrodesis [fusing the bones] of the hip and knee joints. Later, Charnley applied his creative imagination to the problem of the lubrication of joints, the potential of high impact polyethylene and the application of self-curing acrylic cement.

Though a skilled engineer as well as a surgeon, Charnley quickly outran the resources of his own laboratory and it was through his close co-operation with Thackray and his company's engineers that low-friction total hip replacement was gradually perfected."

The tailor-made hip

Different designs of off-the-shelf femoral stems proliferated, but an exact fit for each patient would have necessitated keeping in stock literally hundreds of different stems at any one time, owing to the unique shape of each patient's bones. This problem had been overcome in the past either by standardising the shape of the cavity or by the use of cement to wedge the nearest-available shape stem into the patient's thigh bone.

Ironically it was the very success of the cemented Charnley stem which led to a search for a non-cemented one, for the increased proven life of the product encouraged operations to be performed in younger patients. However, this in turn increased the risk of the eventual deterioration of the cement/bone interface, leading to loosening of the stem. This condition required another operation which was much more exacting than the original implantation. Several non-cemented hips were devised to overcome this difficulty but the results were poor owing to only a minor proportion of the stem being in contact with the surrounding bone.

33. The Identifit hip. This was a revolutionary answer to the problem of loosening of cemented hips because it was made to fit individual patients while still on the operating table.

85

A revolutionary solution to the problem was devised by a Belgian orthopaedic surgeon, Professor Joseph Mulier, from the University of Leuven, who approached Thackray's with his concept of a made-to-measure stem. Such was the company's reputation in the orthopaedic field that he chose Thackray's in preference to any other, including the American giants. An additional benefit of selecting a relatively small company, such as Thackray's, was that it was likely to offer the surgeon a greater degree of control than its larger competitors. Mulier's idea was for an implant that needed no cement, manufactured while the patient was still on the operating table.

Together, Mulier and Thackray's developed the system called Identifit. During this operation, a mould was made by injecting a fast-setting substance into the femoral cavity; the mould was then transferred to the Identifit unit close to the operating theatre. Surgery could continue with the fixing of the cup.

Meanwhile, the mould was measured accurately using laser technology, and the measurements from the laser scan were relayed to a computer. The computer processed the data to a milling machine fitted with a suitable titanium blank, a rough form selected by X-ray. When the milling was finished, the stem was inspected, sterilized and passed to the surgeon to insert into the bone. A separate head to the stem, with a choice of diameter and neck length adjustment, was attached separately. It took about forty minutes from the measuring of the mould to the delivery of the implant, which surgeons found acceptable, but this time is being further reduced by improvements in computer and manufacturing methods.

The first stem to be inserted in a patient this way was in February 1987. Of sixteen patients operated on more than a year previously who had a cemented Charnley stem inserted on one side and a non-cemented Identifit stem on the other, only two found the cemented side better. The economical advantage of the system is twofold: it is not necessary to stock scores of different sized stems and a suitable implant is readily available even for unpredictable revision cases.

CHAPTER 10

The Third Generation

It was in the prosperous years of the 1960s that the third generation of the family, John and his cousin Paul Thackray, entered the picture. Tod's son, John, had spent his "gap" year between Charterhouse School and Cambridge University serving the first year of an apprenticeship on the shopfloor at Viaduct Road, and he rejoined the firm after gaining his Economics degree. But he was understandably reluctant to settle down to the career in manufacturing that already seemed to have been mapped out for him; after all, this was the Sixties, when other people his age had shoulder-length hair and were joining *hari krishna* groups.

John's way out was to persuade the company to send him for management training. It is worth remembering that such courses were far less common in the 1960s than they are today; his departure from the tradition of learning the business from within the company represented the beginning of a process that was to change the whole style of management in the 1970s.

John says he learnt a lot from his spell away from the firm, first on a course at Edinburgh University where he had the opportunity of exchanging ideas with young managers from other countries, especially the USA, and then from fifteen months' working in Amsterdam for a market research company called Westermarkt, a subsidiary of the J. Walter Thompson advertising group.

Noel's son, Paul, had intended to work for the firm only temporarily, having returned from army service abroad - working in a garrison medical centre - following his education at Malvern College. However, after a stint in the firm doing jobs which ranged from order assembly and checking to tea-making, his interest in Thackray's products grew. Deciding to stay on, he gained experience in different departments, including a year in the London office and a spell as a representative. (Twenty years or so later, Paul's son, Craig, was to follow a broadly similar pattern. Joining the firm straight from school, he developed an

34. Princess Marina, accompanied by Sir Cecil Wakeley - past President of the Royal College of Surgeons - is shown some of Thackray's products by Paul Thackray at a nursing exhibition in 1965.

interest in the medical field while employed in the London office and then with Thackray's Irish distributor in Dublin. He went on to work with the new Identifit system in Belgium and the USA, putting his aptitude for computers to good use.)

When John rejoined Paul in the family firm in the Sixties, all was going exceptionally well for the business. The dramatic increase in demand at home created by the extensive hospital-building programme coincided with a surge of new hospitals in the oil-rich countries.

Thackray's had enjoyed the benefits of a captive market in the British Empire since the 1920s, as had other major names in the field. By the 1960s, orders from Crown agents in the colonies had obviously dwindled and the Empire countries moved away from Britain as their source of supply, but new markets had been vigorously pursued by Thackray's salesforce so that at this time annual exports were about equal to home sales.

The size of some of the contracts won is noteworthy: for example, in 1968 Thackray's won a multi-thousand pound order to equip a new hospital in British Honduras with everything from surgical instruments to kitchens and curtains; in 1971 a new hospital at Dubai, one of the Arabian Gulf states, ordered £100,000 worth of Thackray's equipment for four new operating theatres and a new built-in theatre system that the company had developed in the UK. Exports did so well that they totalled £1,340,000 in 1971 - largely due to Charnley products - compared with just under £250,000 in 1960, an achievement recognised beyond the firm: Export Director Bill Piggin was awarded the OBE for his services to Britain's sales overseas.

The Seventies: management revolution

Towards the end of the successful Sixties, two factors were responsible for sounding alarm bells in the boardroom. One was the impending abolition of resale price maintenance, which would hit consumables and result in competitors taking over the wholesaling of general sundries, the bulk of Thackray's business; the other was the threat of losing the US agencies, which had been such a profitable source of income since the 1920s, as American companies set up their own operations here.

First, the board recognised the need to update its methods. Top of the agenda was stock control. Many long-established systems in the company had become hopelessly out of date as the firm had grown, so that, for example, one order comprising several different items would have to be handled by each department concerned - and this at a time when there were about 15,000 different product lines stored at three different warehouses, in Leeds, London and Glasgow. The system made it almost impossible to keep track of orders and resulted in poor delivery dates to the customer. Competitors who had already modernised their warehousing in terms of storage and computerisation could offer same-day delivery, so it was clear that Thackray's would have to bring their methods up to date.

Computerisation was going to be an essential part of streamlining, particularly in stock control, which was a major problem for the company. A large amount of capital was invested in stock, as much as twelve to eighteen months' worth at any given time, and there were thousands of different product lines to keep track of. Outside computer consultants were brought in to ease the transition to a computerised system. To begin with, invoices, purchase orders and delivery notes were all that the company attempted to put on computer. There was, as yet, no method of linking them into accounts, for instance.

Most members of staff who worked for Thackray's at this time agree that the company's first taste of modernity was a fiasco. Most of the problems were blamed on "the computer", and employees' overriding memory is of pushing pieces of paper around to no apparent benefit. "If I had ordered what the computer had said on day one," claimed someone in the purchasing department, "Thackray's would have been bankrupt. There were over 7000 purchase orders on the computer, compared to the 30 or 40 we normally had a day."

Some staff, who endured two years' stress and late working, blamed computer experts for not listening to their advice when the programs were being set up. However, as Thackray's had no satisfactory interdepartmental system even on paper, creating a system on computer was doomed to confusion.

The extra work created in putting right mistakes resulting from the first stumbling steps into computerisation was considerable for some. Not least for Noel Thackray, who had been closely involved with the whole programme since its introduction. Members of his family feel that that period of stress and overwork made him ill and probably even hastened his death in 1970.

35. Tod Thackray became sole Managing Director when his brother, Noel, died in 1970. Here he is with his son, John, the third generation of Thackrays to join the firm.

36. This 1970s aerial photograph (the opposite view to the one on page 68) shows how Thackray's had expanded since acquiring the Beeston site, both in terms of factory space, left, and a new 30,000 sq ft (3,000 sq m) warehouse, bottom right.

His son Paul has vivid recollections of those two years; he worked weekends and up to five hours' overtime every day trying to sort out the mayhem.

To blame the computer, as everybody did, was not entirely fair: the problems really lay in haphazard methods of stock control and the staff's lack, through no fault of their own, of computer know-how. For example, in the continence products department, where stock had been the responsibility of a lady called Nellie Newell, affectionately known as "Rubber Nellie" throughout the firm, items were re-ordered on the simple basis of gaps on shelves. Confusion over quantities - where, for example, Thackray's pack sizes differed from those listed by the manufacturer - frequently led to vast over-ordering.

Despite the problems, computerisation had been a necessity where so many different product lines were stocked, but success was possible only with purpose-built storage. A new warehouse constructed at the Beeston site in 1974 eventually brought the efficiency that had been hoped for.

On Noel's death, Tod, with whom he had run the company for sixteen years, took his place as Chairman and Managing Director. Vacating his office at Beeston, Tod came to the Old Medical School in Park Street to take over what had traditionally been

91

the managing director's office, leaving no one in any doubt as to who was now in the driving seat.

Noel had been in the habit of lunching with his fellow Park Street directors. Tod, meanwhile, out on a limb a couple of miles away at Beeston, could not join the rest regularly for lunch and therefore had not been party to many of their discussions. Although he had nominally been Joint Managing Director with Noel, there was no doubt in most people's minds that Tod had been overshadowed by his older brother. Now he had to make it clear that he was in charge. His customary diffidence gave way to a new-found confidence, and he flourished in his new role, in which he was supported by his son John and his nephew Paul, both already directors of the company.

Tod had been running the manufacturing and sales side of Thackray's instruments and equipment; together with Sidney Beardmore's marketing skills, he had succeeded in keeping Thackray's name at the forefront - a vital key to the sales of Thackray's other goods which rode on the back of orders for their renowned instruments.

As we have seen in the previous section, Tod had built up a good relationship with Charnley, both through their copious correspondence and through Tod's visits to Wrightington. Since Charnley implants and their associated instrumentation repre- sented a substantial slice of Thackray's business at this time, it was important that their relationship with this demanding surgeon should not be jeopardised. To his credit, Tod handled Charnley - a top surgeon used to getting his own way - with tact and patience, though he did not shy away from replying to criticism robustly, too.

Although no one could argue that the bottom line of the company's accounts did not show a healthy profit as the Sixties gave way to the Seventies, both John, brimming with new ideas from his management training, and Paul, impressed by the organisation he had experienced in the armed forces, felt that the administration of the company was old-fashioned and inefficient. Those involved in management had not had the advantage of outside experience, having mostly learnt the job within the company, starting as apprentices or pharmacists.

There was a tendency to confuse activity with importance so that, for example, although 75 percent of Thackray's business at that time was distributing other people's products, it was the other 25 percent, manufacturing, that took up most boardroom time. In this respect, though, Thackray's was no different from any of the other major surgical houses.

There was criticism of the company's administration from other quarters, too. This letter was written by Charnley to one of Thackray's managers in January, 1968:

"I am writing this letter confidentially to you, arising out of a remark that it appears you dropped ... at the recent visit [to Wrightington], namely that the whole firm of Thackray's would get a new lease of life if it could be 'taken over'. The reason I am taking a long shot in writing to you confidentially on this subject is because I have at the moment in hospital, as a private patient, Lord Netherthorpe who is Chairman of Fisons and has some 20 or 30 companies under his control. He is doing very well after his arthroplasty, so far, and he's extremely impressed with the surgery he has received. If you really think a takeover would be in the best interests of Thackray's, and of the export of British surgical instruments on a commercial basis, I could take the opportunity of sowing the seed in Lord Netherthorpe's mind. They already have an instrument division which makes highly specialised automatic apparatus for chemical analysis which is used in up-to-date pathological laboratories."

There is no record of a reply to this letter, but Charnley's suggestion was evidently not pursued.

Noel and Tod had encouraged their sons to play a full part in management and the cousins' roles complemented one another throughout their careers with the firm: John, the big-strategy man, Paul, homing in on the detail. John's management training had convinced him that Thackray's lacked professionally trained managers. When he suggested bringing in management consultants, Tod welcomed the idea. It was at this point that Thackray's had their first contact with Ron Frank, lecturer in management studies at Leeds Polytechnic, whose role has already been touched on in relation to Charnley.

Frank's first report for the company, on production and how it should be organised, underlined the need for a high grade of works manager. On the strength of his recommendations, Jim

Boyd was appointed to carry out the reorganisation needed. He masterminded a huge reduction in the number of processes needed to produce Charnley implants and instigated a massive investment in machinery leading to what became unquestionably the most efficient production line of stems in the world.

While Charnley implants represented the bulk of Thackray's orthopaedic business, it should not be forgotten that many other distinguished orthopaedic surgeons were developing new designs with the company. Among these were trauma products associated with bone fractures, and knee and elbow joint replacements which, owing to their complex shape, had to be cast rather than cold worked like the hip prostheses. The highly specialised process of casting to a high degree of metallurgical integrity was carried out by a Thackray subsidiary, Aeromed, at Rotherham in South Yorkshire.

Ron Frank, who so far had acted as an outside consultant for Thackray's, was asked to join the firm soon after Jim Boyd's arrival in 1971. John Thackray admits that he and Paul had little business experience at the time and that Ron Frank taught them a lot. Further advice was sought from others in Leeds Polytechnic's Department of Management, whose brief was to look at marketing. Their report made it clear that the firm had no concerted approach to marketing and that if action were not taken quickly, the healthy position that Thackray's was in owing to a favourable market environment could soon revert to one of chaos or even decline.

From today's standpoint, when such things as corporate planning would be taken for granted in any company the size of Thackray's, the lack of any overall strategy that existed might seem remarkable. However, the company's apparent lack of cohesion is explained when looked at in historical context. As joint Managing Directors, Tod and Noel had developed a harmonious working relationship and had looked after their respective areas successfully. Broadly speaking, Noel oversaw Park Street activities, with a particular enthusiasm for imported agencies, and had overall responsibility for sales and marketing. Tod was in charge of Viaduct Road and Beeston, including the manufacture and sale of instruments, pharmaceuticals and tubular steel furniture, the latter his particular forte. But neither had the confidence to cross disciplines and nor did any other director.

94

(One board member went so far as to describe directors' meetings at that time as farcical because no one wished to raise matters that could be construed as lapses of management in another's area. That just wasn't cricket.)

The fundamental flaw in Thackray's management structure was that it was linear, with everyone reporting to one man in their department, rather than pyramidal, with each employee answerable to an immediate superior. And why should anything change? The annual accounts continued to show reasonable profits throughout the 1950s and 60s, even if they gave no idea of the outstanding order book.

Ron Frank put forward a solution to the lack of co-ordination within the firm which was to restructure the business. The old "shop" system - in which, for example, each department had its own raw materials store, even though many items were common to other departments - was consequently replaced by a new structure, in which the company was divided by function rather than product. Thus accounts, data processing and personnel became the new Services Division; Manufacturing - with its own personnel department - became another; marketing, sales and order processing of other product groupings (except Raymed) were incorporated into another division called Thackray Trading. To put the reorganisation into practice ten new managers were appointed in the early 1970s and, as John Thackray put it, "The driving was left to them."

The revolution occurring within the company at the turn of the decade was mirrored elsewhere, with people working shorter hours and trade unions' influence on industry increasing. It was at this point that John feels the company ceased to be a patriarchy, and for the first time a personnel manager was appointed.

Socially things were changing, too. Thackray's was forced to discontinue the annual dinner-dance as there was now simply nowhere large enough to entertain the 700 employees and their families.

The 1970s saw the company's first strike. This was a remarkable event in a business with no record of industrial action throughout its long history, but less noteworthy when considered in the national context. Throughout the country, millions of workers had been given a cost-of-living increase in the high-inflation days of the mid 1970s, and about 300 of the workforce at Beeston walked out in protest at the delay in payment of their threshold award. Union members agreed to return to work after twelve days when they were offered a cost-of-living safeguard.

The otherwise good record of labour/management relations survived this hiccup and the Seventies continued to be a prosperous decade for the company. Widespread hospital building, with concomitant orders for new equipment, was good for business, and increasing profits from the sale of Charnley products were ploughed back into the company.

Facing up to radical change

Towards the end of the Seventies, John and Paul Thackray took over as Managing Director and Deputy respectively, while Tod remained as Chairman. Broadly speaking, John took responsibility for sales and marketing, Paul for purchasing.

John Thackray remembers it as an exciting, go-ahead period, with large capital investment, increased manufacturing activity and building-up of overseas sales - a confidence reflected, perhaps, by the firm's first publication of glossy literature to supplement its catalogues. A vigorous marketing policy, identifying what people wanted and making it, undoubtedly contributed to the success of the Seventies.

Much of the marketing spadework was undertaken by John, who at this time was travelling for as much as a third of the year and reckons he visited about 100 countries between the mid Seventies and the mid Eighties. It was hard work and not without its problems. Once, having dozed off in Jedda's airport lounge, John had his passport stolen and was forced to remain in Saudi Arabia. Unfortunately, this was at the time of the Helen Smith affair (which involved the questionable circumstances surrounding the death in Saudi of a young Leeds nurse); the Lebanese owner of the hotel where John had been staying was so frightened of repercussions from the Saudi authorities that he was reluctant to let this English businessman stay unless John would say he had "lost" his passport. A replacement was sent from the UK within a week, and John was deported from the country.

96

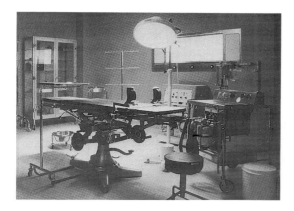

37. This operating theatre in a Middle Eastern private hospital, equipped by Thackray's, is typical of contracts fulfilled by the Interplan Division in the 1970s and 80s.

The new approach to marketing built on the successes of the overseas contracts won in the Sixties. It led to some substantial export orders, particularly to the Middle East. Interplan Hospital Projects Division secured orders worth hundreds of thousands of pounds for equipment for Middle Eastern hospitals and in 1978 Interplan won a £2½ million contract for a royal hospital, containing an operating theatre, X-ray department and laboratory, in Abu Dhabi. It was the first time the firm had scheduled such a project from start to finish, with Thackray consultants going out to the United Arab Emirates to discuss products and assess the logistics of supply.

Despite the high turnover achieved in some of the early capital projects, contracts sometimes included only a small minority of Thackray products, with much equipment, including such diverse items as curtains and easy chairs, bought in. The package equipping business was full of pitfalls, not least of which was the obligation in many overseas countries to deal with a middleman whose honesty could not be relied on.

The nature of Thackray's business meant that they were sometimes called on to meet emergency contracts. In 1977, a Ghanaian hospital requested urgent delivery of sterilizing equipment, and staff at the Beeston factory responded by working day and night, including weekends, to fulfil the contract for eight autoclaves in record time. A Thackray installation engineer flew to West Africa ahead of the equipment to ensure that the site and services were ready and to supervise the off-loading and installation of the equipment.

Another emergency request was answered the following year

and under the headline, "City firm's mercy dash saves heart girl's life", the *Yorkshire Evening Post* printed the following story:

"A Leeds-based medical equipment manufacturer's desperate race against time has saved the life of a critically-ill child in a Paris hospital. Charles F. Thackray Ltd were called on to supply vital heart valves for the child because suppliers in France and Belgium were out of stock.

"Mr Dennis Craven, the firm's shipping manager, said they had first promised to put the valves on the first available flight the following morning but were told the child would be dead by then. Despite terrible congestion at Manchester Airport because of the French air-traffic controllers action they managed to get an aeroplane to take the valves earlier. A Thackray's worker raced to the airport but was stopped on the way for speeding.

" 'However, when he told the officers of the cause, he was given an 80 miles an hour [130 kph] police escort,' said Mr Craven. The same night, the valves arrived in Paris and the operation was successful."

The company's philanthropic side is less publicised, but through ECHO (Equipment for Charity Hospitals Overseas), in the 1980s it donated something in the region of £50,000 worth of supplies annually to hospitals in developing countries. Thackray's instruments and medical equipment have played a part in projects such as an expedition led by Chris Bonnington to the south west face of Everest in 1972, and in Operation Raleigh, a round-the-world voyage involving young people.

The largest volume of sales in the Seventies was still in surgical sundries for which there was now cut-throat competition. But, as Paul Thackray put it, "We were like a corner shop trying to compete with supermarkets." If Thackray's were to remain competitive, they would have to specialise. Management was faced with the choice of where investment of money and effort should be concentrated.

They decided to stop competing with the giant distributors of hospital consumables and to rationalise their agencies, retaining only exclusive ones or those that complemented their own theatre products.

As it was, the company was fully stretched to meet orders for its own products. Although the average time taken to supply the

38. Hand forging. This process continued in the production of short run, specialist instruments both at Beeston in Leeds and Thomas Selby & Son in London until the late 1970s. The relationship between the two firms, dating back to 1908 when Selby first supplied Charles Thackray with instruments, was cemented in 1974 when Thackray's acquired the London firm.

last item on a large order had halved, from twelve months in the Sixties to six months in the Seventies, this compared badly with foreign competition at three months. It was clear that the firm would not be able to meet this competition and the volume of Charnley orders if it did not farm out more products. Therefore the manufacture of some of the more common instruments, such as Moynihan's artery forceps, were subcontracted, together with simple furniture, like dressing trolleys and drip-stands.

This strategy left Thackray's producing a minority of its own instruments for the first time and it opened the way for manufacturing to be concentrated on new winners, like Charnley, and medium-run items such as plastic surgery instruments, whose origins went back to the close relationship established with the world-renowned plastic surgeons Gillies and McIndoe during the Second World War. Thackray's new *modus operandi* could be compared to another highly successful Leeds-born firm,

99

Marks & Spencer, in that they set the quality control and design standards, but contracted others to make the goods.

Charnley products were becoming predominant in total sales, and at the same time cheap surgical instruments from overseas were showing sufficient improvement in quality to satisfy a segment of the market, a factor which had been exacerbated by the removal of resale price maintenance by the government towards the end of the 1960s. Thackray's had always insisted that any product bearing the company's name must be British made (although not necessarily by them), a policy which was partly a relic of the pre-war dependence on British Empire markets, where foreign-made goods carried an unwelcome stigma.

Concerned that the gateways to lower costs should not continue to be closed by this "British made" policy, the board looked at Continental manufacturing. Accordingly, instrument executives visited renowned instrument makers in Tuttlingen, southern Germany, where the world's largest concentration of instrument manufacturers was situated. (Paul Thackray was to make a lasting impression, both literally and metaphorically, on one of these trips which he was in the habit of making in a motorhome. Invited by his German host to park the vehicle on his lawn, Paul found it stuck in the mud next morning.)

German and British instrument quality were similar, but the prices varied. Sheffield suppliers were found to be cheaper on the long-run lines, while Germany, because of its larger exports, was cheaper on the most specialised lines. So where patterns were the same, the company started to import a range of specialist instruments which they marked Thackray Germany. More important, Paul Thackray found suppliers of components which allowed the works and their British subcontractor to reduce costs of the finished products.

Aware that the cost-conscious National Health Service was looking to buy as cheaply as possible, the board considered seriously the question of Thackray's setting up its own manufacturing operation in Pakistan or Sri Lanka. However, it was known from other companies which had tried this that considerable management from head office was required to ensure the necessary control of quality. Paul Thackray felt that the company had not proved it could manage its existing out-of-Leeds operations well, namely in Africa and its subsidiaries in

Sheffield and London, Thomas Rudd and the British Cystoscope Company. He therefore concluded that the firm should leave the cost-cutting market to others, and continue to concentrate on the high-quality instruments on which the company's reputation was founded and which provided the entree to profitable hospital orders.

On the whole, the rationalisation strategies worked, but the decision to retain only exclusive agencies could backfire, as Thackray's found to their cost with an excellent American product, the Shiley Heart Valve. This was a lucrative agency to have acquired: the product took up little stock space, replacements could be delivered from the US within five days, and with a high percentage gross margin on average order values of £300, it achieved a turnover of £1 million. Then, with little warning, the agency was withdrawn and profits for the company were halved overnight.

The Shiley experience led management to become far more cost conscious. It made John Thackray realise that he and his fellow directors would have to adopt a tougher approach and to take some radical, and sometimes unpopular, decisions. Among these was the closure of the firm's canteen and, later, the London office.

At the end of the successful Seventies, an overvalued pound hit exports, and cash limits were imposed on the National Health Service. For the first time, profits dropped to break even. This marked the beginning of a recession that characterised the first years of the Eighties. In common with the rest of industry, Thackray's found themselves having to make staff redundant, dropping from a total 750 employed to 500 over a period of three or four years. However, the number of compulsory redundancies was small, some employees retiring a couple of years early and others not replaced when jobs became superfluous.

In a constantly-developing industry, it was going to be essential for the firm to develop a dynamic structure capable of accommodating regular change. Management realised the necessity of involving the workforce in its decisions and consequently a monthly forum, known as the Consultative Council, was set up to facilitate communication between the company and employees.

The forum was soon to prove invaluable with the next major reorganisation of the company, which involved separating Orthopaedics from Instruments and splitting the Pharmaceutical Division.

John Thackray had for some time been concerned that the improved methods of manufacturing Charnley hips and increased sales did not show through to the end profit of the company. It was unlikely that the root cause could be established unless the activities associated with orthopaedics could be measured separately. Isolating orthopaedics would be advantageous, too, in trying to overcome the formidable difficulties of selling Charnley products in any quantity in the States, with the need to develop big-budget, American-style marketing. Accordingly, the Thackray Trading Division - which encompassed orthopaedics, instruments, surgical furniture, electro-surgical apparatus, sterilizing equipment and sundry distributorships - was split into two to become the Orthopaedics and Surgery divisions.

A development programme involving substantial investment in Orthopaedics followed. To some extent, Charnley's death in 1982 released the company from some of the constraints imposed by the surgeon and gave them a freer hand to develop new designs for knee and hip replacements, culminating in the revolutionary Orthogenesis project, led by the Identifit system. With a turnover of £20 million by the mid Eighties, Orthopaedics represented the lion's share of Thackray's business; in 1985 the company set up direct sales operations in the USA and, four years later, in Australia.

Meanwhile, the Surgery Division was due for radical reorganisation. Many instruments were now bought in, from Germany and Britain, and sterilizers and hospital furniture continued to be made at little or no profit - a fact that had been known to the board for some time but never acted on for fear of upsetting customers and staff and because a relatively high value of sterilizing components would have to have been written off. In the event, when the decision to discontinue the manufacture of sterilizers was at last taken, the marketplace hardly noticed. In the next six months operating tables and other furniture were subcontracted. Staff retrained for Charnley products and one or two joined the subcontractors so that the question of personnel conflicts did not arise. Subsequently, at least 1,000 other items were discontinued, dramatically reducing administration costs and stockholding.

The drug department was also in trouble. Raymed (its name an amalgamation of Thack*ray med*ical), which had had a good turnover and had shown healthy growth under Joe Colehan's management, was becoming less and less profitable. Raymed's origins lay in the supply of wholesale pharmaceuticals to private nursing homes and general practitioners all over the North of England. Uneconomical though it was, Thackray's continued supplying its loyal customers in this way until as recently as 1983, but eventually Raymed's balance sheet could not be ignored.

It became clear that to make the division profitable, fewer products and larger volumes would be needed. In this light, infection control was seen as the way forward. Hospital pharmacies, which in the past had made their own cleansing preparations, were closing down; in addition, there were only one or two companies manufacturing any given product in the field of infection control, compared to the already overpopulated area of curative products.

The re-vamped pharmaceutical division was transformed into Pearce Laboratories (Pearce having been Helen Thackray's maiden name and inherited by both Tod and John Thackray as a middle name) and transferred to new premises at Garforth on the outskirts of Leeds. Here, the division concentrated its efforts on manufacturing spirit-based disinfectants, such as chlorhexidine, and lubricating and ultrasound gels. The large volumes produced meant that Thackray's could outprice many of its giant competitors in this field. Dividing bulk products into ward packs for hospital use also proved to be a successful strategy.

The reorganisation of Thackray Trading and of Raymed - effectively splitting the division into Pearce Laboratories on the one hand, and ostomy and continence products (under the heading Thackraycare) on the other - marked the beginning of a new policy which could conveniently, if clumsily, be called divisionalisation.

Thackray's had in the past been divided by product, then by discipline (sales, marketing and so on). The Eighties programme of divisionalisation meant a return to division by product area, with each division having its own manufacturing, warehouse, sales and marketing, but with the additional advantage of shared, centralised services. The divisionalisation programme led to the unavoidable redundancies of a director and two managers, an unprecedented event at Thackray's and a measure of what was involved.

The major reorganisation of Thackray's reflected the new, bolder approach John and Paul had developed towards managing the company. They felt they had for too long been dictated to: by distributors deciding market prices, by Charnley browbeating them to get what he wanted. It was time to express their own opinions more forcefully and run the company their way. They had acquired the confidence that comes with experience.

Expansion

The development programme instigated in Orthopaedics required more space at the works. Expansion at Beeston was financed by the sale of the Old Medical School which, fortuitously, Leeds City Council was keen to purchase as part of a redevelopment scheme. The Park Street premises had been justifiably criticised for their cramped conditions. The maze-like interior which had developed over many years of alterations had done nothing for discipline either, making it easy for staff to lose themselves if they wanted to for large parts of the day in the building. Despite its disadvantages, Park Street was nonetheless held in affection by many, not least because the company's occupation of the building spanned all the generations: first, Chas. F. Thackray himself with Scurrah Wainwright, and Mercer Gray; then Thackray's sons, Noel and Tod; Wainwright's son, Richard, and Mercer Gray's son Robert; then the third generation, Noel and Tod Thackray's sons, Paul and John, and Robert Gray's children, Janet and Michael.

The Old Medical School building was demolished to make way for additions to the Magistrate's Court, but not before Robert Gray had had the elaborately decorated glass door panels (illustrated on page 38) removed from the front entrance. The panels were put on display at the firm's head office, where Paul Thackray had set up a permanent exhibition of antique medical instruments and pharmaceutical artefacts.

Leeds City Council's approach to Thackray's to buy the site fortunately coincided with the need to find larger premises anyway. The Council, victim of Government's insistence that any unspent money be returned to the Treasury at the end of each financial year, found itself with half a million pounds unspent in March. They offered Thackray's an attractive price (for which the firm had been hoping for years) on the strict condition that the entire transaction was completed and all deeds passed into Council ownership within *three weeks*. Having negotiated a period in which the company could stay on while it looked for an alternative, this was duly done.

The proceeds enabled the Beeston expansion to be carried out and a lease was acquired on a new brick-built building in Shire Oak Street, Headingley, on the edge of Leeds, for Thackray's new head office.

Meanwhile, the remarkable growth of Thackraycare was a success story in its own right and is described separately in the following chapter.

CHAPTER 11

Thackraycare

The firm's tradition of service to the customer was taken into new fields with the birth of Thackraycare in 1974. Devised by Christin Thackray (a qualified theatre nurse who met her husband, John, when she was working for a company distributing Charnley products in her native Norway), Thackraycare was created in response to two major factors in patient care in the community: first, the trend towards shorter hospital stays, necessitating an increase of health care in the community, and second, the ageing population with its attendant needs.

Thackraycare set out not only to sell rehabilitation aids for various physical handicaps and chronic conditions, but also to change the image and style of service of dispensing appliance contractors. Fundamental to the new approach was a scheme to employ trained nurses to fit appliances and to give a back-up service and advice.

The idea for the service, Christin says, "arose from a visit I paid to the orthopaedic shop in Great George Street [which remained at no. 52 after the retail pharmacy shop had closed] when there was talk of closing it. On the day I went in, there was a patient who had had a colostomy twenty years previously and said she had been making do with cotton wool and plastic bags since her operation. I was appalled and felt we must be able to do something better for patients like her. I could see an obvious gap in services which Thackray's would be well placed to fill."

At that time, patients simply went to the retail shop and had their prescriptions dispensed from Thackray's own range of manufactured appliances. As a former nurse, Christin took an interest in the people who used the shop and realised that they were in need of far more professional help and advice than was available to them. It was this realisation that gave rise to the entirely new concept of specialist care centres where patients could be assessed and fitted professionally - not just from the comparatively limited range of Thackray products, but from the full Drug Tariff approved list of 3,500 products.

To get her idea off the ground, Christin felt that her first job was to persuade the company, which at the time was product orientated, to provide the product and service direct to the consumer rather than via the surgeon and wholesaler. The Raymed Division was making appliances, but its products were being sold into hospitals by representatives so that the expertise for fitting and advice was not reaching the patient in the community. With hospitals discharging patients as soon as possible after treatment, there was clearly a need for professional support for patients once they returned home.

District nurses and staff in health centres were interested in the idea but were sceptical because they saw the business as commercial rather than service related. It took five years to convey the concept that a commercial company could be professional too. By the beginning of 1980, Thackraycare took on its first two nurses to put the concept into practice.

The next step was to try to change the image of the old shop. The Orthopaedic department - all brown paint and cracked lino - was a relic from the retail shop days; it had been at the back of the pharmacy, with a separate entrance in Great George Street and remained when the shop was sold. Christin Thackray was given control of the Orthopaedic department and the front shop in Park Street. Thackray diagnostic products were also displayed in the basement of Thackray's Instrument Centre, which had been at 47 Great George Street since 1978. Doctors visiting either of the instrument showrooms were therefore made aware of Thackray's other services.

It was the first time that patient appliances (including incontinence, ostomy and laryngectomy products, trusses, surgical stockings and dressings), which until then had been more or less kept under the counter, were properly and attractively displayed. Christin's experience in urology in a Norwegian hospital was significant in this fresh approach: she was shocked at the way patients were treated and brought a much more open way of thinking to patients who had to come to terms with wearing a medical appliance.

In 1982, negotiations were finalised to take over no. 45, the shop next door to the Instrument Centre. A new Care Centre was opened, with both shops sharing an elegant nineteenth-century frontage. What Christin had learnt from serving customers in

39. Christin Thackray. Her idea of sending trained nurses to patients' homes, rather than selling appliances to wholesalers or over the counter, revolutionised continence care.

the old shop she hoped to put into practice in the new centre. She was determined to change the image of the old appliance contractor, and took care that the new premises were decorated in a style that would avoid an institutional atmosphere and that would appeal to all age groups.

Thackraycare had contracts with Family Practitioner Committees to dispense doctors' prescriptions and each of its centres was approved as a Dispensing Appliance Contractor. Most manufacturers' products were stocked and it was strict policy to give unbiased advice and recommend a Thackray product only where appropriate.

The success of the centre lay in word-of-mouth recommendation and by 1984, Thackray's felt ready to open others. First, they acquired a centre in Surrey and the same year took over another in Bristol. Two years later, in 1986, another centre was acquired in Oxford, followed by others in Southampton and Wolverhampton.

The proliferation of the Thackraycare centres could never have happened, in Christin Thackray's view, without the commitment of the SRN and RGN qualified nurses who worked in the field. They were faced with selling the new concept to a sometimes conservative medical profession, and their belief in what they were doing was vital to the project's success.

When the first Thackraycare shop opened in Leeds, there were no guidelines for appliance contractors, although appliance suppliers had been in existence before the NHS was created in 1948. They had traditionally supplied calipers, surgical stockings, trusses and so on to hospitals. Chemists could supply appliances on repeat prescription, but they did not have the expertise in assessment, fitting and management. Patients could not easily ask a pharmacist's advice in a busy shop; they wanted to choose in comfort, and in privacy, from a specialist.

Most patients were referred to Thackraycare by healthcare professionals in the community and most - as many as 90 per cent - were seen in their own homes. Home visits were an immeasurable improvement for patients: nurses did not leave consultations until they felt that the patient was confident in the use of their appliance; dignity, in what could be a humiliating condition for some, could be preserved; and patients felt secure in the knowledge that the nurse would make follow-up visits. The shops, meantime, took on the role of resource centres, where patients and doctors could call in and talk to the nurses - or appliance practitioners, as they became known - both to ask advice and to give progress reports.

Meanwhile, the precise role of appliance contractors was still unclear. "As a member of the British Surgical Trades Association [BSTA]," said Christin Thackray, "I had talked to them about the concept of opening a centre which would promote not only our own products but others, too, to give patients the maximum choice of what was available. I also went to five other

40. The Instrument and Care Centres in Great George Street. With the opening of the Care Centre in 1982 patient appliances were properly displayed for the first time.

contractors who saw the idea in a positive light. Together, we drafted a Code of Practice for Appliance Contractors." A code which, guided by Ron Frank, was carried through the BSTA and adopted in 1986/7.

As a dispenser of drugs and surgical appliances, Thackray's came under the same legal umbrella as dispensing chemists and was therefore prohibited from advertising. This ruling presented a problem: it meant that Thackray's could not even leave patients with an explanatory leaflet after a consultation because it would be considered unethical. It was equally clear, though, that patients wanted this sort of information. The solution was a leaflet that explained the role of appliance centres to which patients could go for advice - an answer to the problem which neatly fell in with the government's encouragement to extend patient choice. The Family Practitioner Committees welcomed the development, on the understanding that the Code of Practice would be adopted by that part of the trade.

In the course of the 1980s, the emergence of continence advisers as a new profession, educating the public in the management of incontinence and removing old taboos which were all too common in this field, led to an expanding period for Thackraycare, whose own nurses gave a complementary service to continence advisers employed by the NHS. This co-operation culminated, in march 1990, in the first national course for appliance practitioners, organised jointly by the Association of Continence Advisers (part of the Royal College of Nursing) and the British Surgical Trades Association. The aim of the three-day course in Newcastle was to help participants with their assessment, selection, application and subsequent management of incontinence appliances, so the bringing together of the professional and commercial branches was invaluable.

Thackraycare's uninterrupted progress from its inception was due largely to the vision and energy of Christin Thackray, whose managerial talents surprised even her husband, John: "I didn't know I had married such a dynamic businesswoman," he said. Christin, for her part, emphasised the role played by Thackraycare's team of committed nurses working in the community.

In addition to the care centres, Christin Thackray had responsibility for the wholesale business of the products. Highest turnover was in the field of incontinence - and, to a lesser extent, ostomy - products, with diagnostic and home-care aids (such as nebulisers for asthma control, glucometers and blood strips for diabetics, together with convalescent room furniture, commodes and so forth) representing a smaller proportion.

CHAPTER 12

A Change of Ownership

From the early years of this century, Thackray's had been involved in the manufacturing and wholesaling of pharmaceuticals and surgical instruments, although the techniques involved and the sheer size of the operation ninety years on would surely have surprised even the firm's founders, however ambitious and optimistic they might have been.

From the Great George Street pharmacy, with its instrument workshop at the back, the firm grew to include manufacturing operations at three different sites in Leeds, another in Rotherham, one at Tweedbank in Scotland and another in London. (The group's activities are summarised in the Appendix.)

At the end of the 1980s, shareholders considered how the firm was to continue into the Nineties and beyond. As a predominantly orthopaedic business, accounting for about eighteen percent of the total number of hips implanted internationally (excluding the USA), John and Paul Thackray recognised that if the company were to compete successfully in the future, they would have to develop a global presence. In practice, this would mean having direct sales operations in most major industrialised countries. The trade with the European Community that 1992 promised would give multinational companies an additional advantage in the world marketplace.

There was also going to be a requirement for deep research into new materials, especially as Charnley products would probably be superseded by something else in the next five to ten years. High technology research is expensive and can, after all, come to nothing. The substantial sums needed to carry out a research programme would have meant either borrowing heavily or finding a partner.

In addition, the board could foresee potential inheritance tax problems arising for individual shareholders as the company grew and became more profitable.

Given these circumstances, most boards of directors would

consider either going public or selling out. The first option was rejected because the family directors felt themselves to be unsuited to the different disciplines the stock market would have imposed. In addition, the British stock market had little track record of medical companies, so there was every likelihood that Thackray's would be undervalued in comparison with American prices.

The other option, selling the company, did not appeal to John and Paul either at that time; they had not planned to retire for another five to ten years. Michael Gray, as company secretary and the only other full-time family director (though younger), would be in a similar position. However, Thackray's was regularly approached by potential buyers - global companies with an interest in orthopaedics - to whom a standard reply was sent, stating that the company was not selling but that interested parties would be informed if there was any change of heart.

Although a sale was not envisaged until the mid-1990s or possibly 2000, the company actually changed hands in 1990. What led to this unexpected turn of events?

Orthogenesis was a major investment for the company and it was not going especially well. Despite units being installed at half a dozen sites in the USA, with as many again expected soon, it was proving difficult to tie customers down to a contract quantity that would ensure a profit; most units had not even reached break-even point. Money was needed to develop and market the system; it needed a partner.

A list was therefore drawn up of some of the big names in orthopaedics and, early in 1990, they were approached with a view to developing Orthogenesis as a joint venture, or possibly selling that part of the company - an arrangement that would not affect the core business of Thackray's. But no one was interested in buying only part of the company: all or nothing was the common response.

John and Paul Thackray consulted the board, making it clear that in their view selling the company should be considered only on strict conditions: that a high, US-level price - which meant offers in excess of £80 million - was paid; that the buyer should have a similar ethos, or compatible management style; that continuity of employment on the firm's present sites could be assured for the foreseeable future; that the buyer would continue to expand the company.

With such exacting preconditions for a sale, there were few possible contenders. In fact, the board considered they would be lucky to sell at all in these circumstances. However, a privately-owned British company such as Thackray's was an attractive prospect for potential buyers, with comparatively low labour and social costs (wages, pensions, National Insurance and so on being lower than in most other European countries) and the expertise for producing high quality products. Among the international companies with pharmaceutical or medical interests who showed interest was another family-owned business called Corange.

Corange could provide the worldwide sales and development network, through its subsidiary DePuy, that Thackray's needed. And Corange, with fifty percent of its sales in diagnostic products, twenty percent in pharmaceuticals, another twenty percent in biomaterials, but only ten percent of its worldwide sales

41. The signing of the documents to complete the sale of Thackray's on 30th April 1990. From left: James Lent, President of DePuy; Curt Engelhorn, Chairman of Corange Ltd; John Thackray, Managing Director of Chas F. Thackray Ltd. "Although it is sad that the time has come for the Thackray family to withdraw from personal ownership of our old established firm", said John Thackray, "we do so with no regrets and a feeling that this is not just an appropriate, but also a successful and timely move for all concerned."

in orthopaedics, found what they were looking for in Thackray's.

Despite its French-sounding name, the company was in fact set up in 1859 in Germany, as Boehringer Mannheim, whose origins lay in a pharmacological research laboratory set up by Dr Friedrich Engelhorn in 1889. The company's main product at that time was quinine. Engelhorn's interest lay in synthesizing naturally occurring substances. His laboratory collaborated on the first caffeine synthesis in 1902, and they achieved theophyllum synthesis the following year; other drugs they developed included the first digitalis preparation, in 1919, from which modern digitalis drugs are derived, and later, in 1956, the first oral anti-diabetic agent. Today's international Boehringer Mannheim organisation has grown from this research foundation; it currently researches, develops and manufactures a wide range of health care products, from diagnostics, pharmaceuticals and biochemical technology to instruments and orthopaedic implants.

The name Corange was adopted with changes in equity and management structure in 1985, when the company's headquarters were transferred, for tax reasons, to Bermuda, although their operations were co-ordinated, by a staff of fifty or so, from London. Like Thackray's, the company's shares were still controlled by members of the founding family, the Engelhorns, who had been closely involved with the running of the business since it began.

The choice of the name Corange betrays a sense of humour in the family. It is the Engelhorn name translated into French, with the two syllables transposed: *engel* (angel) is *ange* in French, and horn is translated as *cor*.

The similar pedigree that Thackray's and Corange shared gave the board confidence that a marriage between the two would work, and in April 1990 contracts for the sale of the company were signed. The purchase of Thackray's by a group such as Corange, who own another world leader in orthopaedic manufacture, DePuy of Indiana in the United States, would enable the orthopaedic operations of both companies to expand. By joining forces with DePuy, Thackray's immediately increased its presence in the US, for instance, a hundredfold. And in 1991, foundations were laid for over 100,000 sq ft (15,000 sq m) of new industrial and office space at Beeston.

115

It would be hard to find two manufacturers with as many years' combined experience in the orthopaedic field: DePuy dates back to 1895 (it introduced the first metal splints for supporting broken bones around the turn of the century) and Thackray's began only seven years after that.

Corange's commitment to training, to research and development, and its size - a workforce of 17,000, with subsidiaries, representatives and distributors in more than 100 countries and sales to 141 countries in every continent - provided the worldwide network and financial resources that Thackray's needed to assure the company a future as successful in the twenty-first century as they had been in the twentieth.

Postscript

Under new ownership, and the new name of DePuy, Thackray's workforce remained largely unchanged, although one or two key positions were filled by managers from DePuy in the States.

After a career in the family business, what did John and Paul Thackray do after the sale? John stayed on for a few months in the role of consultant at the new owner's request. The terms of his contract meant, not unnaturally, that for a given period after leaving he could not operate in a field that might compete with theirs (effectively ruling out orthopaedics and incontinence). He therefore chose the highly specialised area of ENT (ear, nose and throat), and head and neck, creating a new company which he called Kapitex, based at Wetherby in North Yorkshire.

Paul's share of the sale proceeds enabled him to develop his long-time interest in the history of pharmacy and medicine, by founding the first national medical museum in the country. After a lengthy search for a suitable home, it was St James's Hospital in Leeds, appropriately, who offered the museum a Grade II listed building they no longer needed. The project attracted a £3 million grant from the Heritage Lottery Fund and the Thackray Medical Museum opened to visitors in March 1997.

Christin Thackray stayed on for eighteen months after the sale, running and further developing Thackraycare, and continuing in the role of consultant for a further eighteen months. She created her own community care company, Medinkonsult, which specialised in continence and stroke care.

Michael Gray, the only other family shareholder working full time for the company, planned to set up his own company, and at the time of writing was exploring a number of options. His father, Bob Gray, continued in retirement his involvement with Leeds Amateur Operatic Society, of which he had been chairman for fourteen years.

Richard Wainwright, financial director until the sale, had retired as Member of Parliament for Colne Valley at the 1987 election, but continued to be actively involved in Liberal Democrat politics and the Charter 88 movement for constitutional reform.

Appendix

In 1990, when the Thackray Group was sold, it comprised the following divisions:

Orthopaedic Division

The largest in the group, this division employed just over 300 staff, 200 of whom were at the Beeston works, out of Thackray's total UK workforce of just over 500. Its dramatic expansion in the Seventies was due largely to the success of the Charnley hip replacement and its accompanying instrumentation, but the Beeston factory was not used solely for the manufacture of Charnley products. Many other distinguished orthopaedic surgeons collaborated with Thackray's to develop new designs.

Second only to hips was the production of knee implants. Replacements for elbows and knees had been developed by surgeons in association with Thackray's bioengineer, Dr Martin Elloy. The knee is one of the most difficult joints to replicate as it involves movement in all planes, but the design problems were overcome in the Total Condylar implant; one model was manufactured for the Japanese market from a design by Professor Yamamoto.

More recently, a revolutionary new design of knee prosthesis, marketed under the name Accord, was developed by an orthopaedic surgeon, R. Johnson, with Dr Elloy. The Accord boasted one of the most extensive clinical histories of any new implant: over 800 were implanted in a trial involving centres in the UK, Holland and Norway, between 1982 and 1989. To achieve the complex geometry required, the knee implant had to be cast, rather than cold-worked like the hip prosthesis. Casting was carried out by Aeromed, at Rotherham in South Yorkshire. A recent development in knee-joint repair was ligament replacement, which underwent its first clinical trials in 1990.

Trauma products were mainly associated with bone fractures. Among these were the Hansson Pin System, designed by Professor Ingvar Hansson of the University of Lund in Sweden, and the Gotfried Nail Plate, both specifically developed for femoral neck fractures. The Shearer External Fixation System, developed in association with Professor John Shearer of Southampton University, enabled adjustments to be made to bone setting after its application. In hand surgery, John Stanley, Consultant Hand Surgeon to the North West Regional Health Authority, designed a system of wrist fusion pins, manufactured by Thackray's.

Complementing the Orthopaedics Division was the arthroscopy range, including telescopes, hand-held cutting instruments, light sources, fibre cables and a powered shaver. On the whole, the powered instruments were factored by Thackray's, while the rigid telescopes and fibre cables for arthroscopy were produced by a Thackray subsidiary, Scope Optics, based in London.

Scope Optics

This small factory in Barnet, North London, had manufactured endoscopes - optical instruments which enable surgeons to investigate organs inside the body through a small aperture - since the early Seventies. Instead of the series of conventional lenses previously used, Scope Optics, in association with Professor Harold Hopkins of the Department of Physics at Reading University, developed a rod lens by which light was transmitted through glass fibres, allowing much smaller instruments to be made. The size of endoscopes has decreased dramatically in recent years, to as small as only 150 microns, or 0.15 millimetres, diameter.

The disciplines of optical physics and electronics required for this sort of development was provided by consultants. The area of research undertaken at the end of the Eighties was directed towards sensors, which have widespread applications, from the high-technology world of communications to the more mundane, in which sensors are used in the accurate positioning of canned food lid seals.

Aeromed

To achieve the complex geometry required, the knee implant had to be cast, rather than cold-worked like the hip prostheses. Casting is a precision process to the extent that its metallurgical integrity must be of sufficient quality that it is free of defects when X-rayed. Aeromed, in which Thackray's had a fifty percent shareholding, had the capability to cast both steel and chrome-cobalt, the latter requiring a particularly high degree of metallurgical control.

Tweedbank Surgical Engineering

Packaging of prostheses took place at this small modern factory, near Galashiels in Scotland, where blister packs and some appliances were manufactured and assembled, together with stomaceuticals (skin care and odour control products), an important element of Thackraycare's business.

Thackraycare

Thackraycare's services have been described in an earlier section but, briefly, their role was to provide a professional post-operative service to patients. Qualified nurses, given further training by Thackray's, visited patients in hospital, and then at home to advise them on the fitting and use of a number of different products associated with continence problems.

From one centre in Leeds, Thackraycare expanded to provide centres throughout the UK.

Pearce Laboratories

The majority of the products manufactured at the Garforth, Leeds factory were used in hospitals, in infection control. They fell into three basic groups: spirit-based disinfectants used in hospitals for instrument and hard-surface disinfection in the operating theatre, together with a red-staining solution for preoperative skin disinfection of the surgery site; chlorhexidine surgical scrub for surgeons' use; disinfectant wipes primarily for hard-surfaces on surgical wards.

A flameproof facility at Garforth ensured that the manufacture of chlorhexidine, which contains highly inflammable methylated spirit and isopropyl alcohol, was carried out safely.

While infection control products, being inflammable, do not travel well, the Division's range of medical lubricating gels, produced in tubes, was suitable for wide distribution, including overseas.

Thackray Surgery

Based at Viaduct Road in Leeds, this division was concerned with design and manufacture in two main areas: instrumentation for fine surgery, such as plastic and maxillo-facial surgery, and patient support, including trolleys, operating tables and so on. (Thackray's MT4 table is displayed in an operating theatre mock-up at the Science Museum in London.) Thackray's continued its tradition of working closely with surgeons to develop their instrumentation and its long-term commitment to customers was shown by the repair service offered, where sometimes instruments as much as 25 years old could be revitalised.

Orthogenesis

Most recent of the Thackray Divisions, Orthogenesis was created to develop the Identifit system. The nature of the system meant that Orthogenesis personnel were located on site, so Orthogenesis companies were set up in each country where an Identifit unit was established, to handle the project. Companies were based at Orlando, Florida, in the USA, in Melbourne, Australia, and Milan in Italy.

Vetbed

Vetbed was acquired in 1987 along with the Garforth factory. Previously run at a loss, Thackray's gave an undertaking to the company's management that they would retain the Vetbed staff and continue production. The seven employees concerned were engaged in making polyester bedding material for pets and veterinary products such as disinfectants, pet wipes and stain removers.

121

References

1. *Chemist and Druggist*, 14 January 1984.
2. *Kelly's Directory of Leeds*, 1902.
3. *Thackray Company Prescription Ledgers*, West Yorkshire Archive Service: Leeds.
4. *Chemist and Druggist*, 3 May 1902.
5. Heap A and Brears P, *Leeds Describ'd*, Breedon Books, 1993.
6. *House Committee Minutes*, Leeds General Infirmary Archive.
7. Anning S T and Walls W K J A, *A History of the Leeds School of Medicine: One and a Half Centuries 1831-1981*, Leeds University Press, 1982.
8. *Reality*, Vol I, issue 2, Sept 1961, Thackray Company Archive, Thackray Medical Museum.
9. Unpublished correspondence, Thackray Company Archive, Thackray Medical Museum.
10. McLeave H, *McIndoe: Plastic Surgeon*, Muller 1961.
11. Mosley L, *Faces from the Fire: The Biography of Sir Archibald McIndoe*, Weidenfeld and Nicholson, 1962.
12. Waugh W, *John Charnley: The Man and the Hip*, Springer-Verlag, 1990.
13. Charnley J, Manchester Collection (Medical), John Rylands University Library of Manchester.

Key Dates

1902	Purchase of retail pharmacy in Great George Street.
1906	Acquisition of steam sterilizer, signalling diversification of business.
1908	Sale of first surgical instruments (supplied by Selby of London). Appointment of firm's first representative. Acquisition of first powered transport, a Triumph motorcycle.
1909	Appointment of Berkeley Moynihan as Professor of Surgery at Leeds University.
1910	Start of instrument repairs. First orders received from Leeds General Infirmary.
1914	Workforce reaches 25, including 3 representatives, 8 surgical instrument makers.
1918	Patent granted for Washington Haigh surgical dressing.
1920s	Start of exporting.
1925	Purchase of Old Medical School in Park Street.
1933	First expansion of Park Street premises.
1934	Death of Chas F. Thackray; appointment of Mercer Gray as Managing Director.
1935	Change of firm's status to a limited company.
1936	Addition of extra storey to Park Street extension.
1937	Publication of first comprehensive catalogue.
1939	Transfer of instrument manufacture to Viaduct Road.
1947	Charnley's first known order from Thackray's.
1948	Introduction of National Health Service.
1945	Creation of South African subsidiary.
1956	Death of Mercer Gray; appointment of Noel and Tod Thackray as joint Managing Directors. Purchase of Beeston factory.
1960s	Start of Charnley hip manufacture.
1961	Acquisition of Thomas Rudd of Sheffield.
1962	Closure of retail shop in Great George Street.
1964	Acquisition of British Cystoscope Co. of London.
1969	Liquidation of South African subsidiary.

1970   Death of Noel Thackray; appointment of Tod Thackray as Chairman and Managing Director.
Appointment of first professionally trained managers.

1974   Founding of Thackraycare.
Construction of new warehouse at Beeston.
Acquisition of Thomas Selby & Son.

1979   Appointment of John Thackray as Managing Director and Paul Thackray, Deputy Managing Director.

1982   Death of Sir John Charnley.
Opening of Care Centre in Great George Street.

1985   Transfer of head office to Shire Oak Street, Headingley.

1987   First implant of tailor-made hip.

1988   Award to Tod Thackray of honorary doctorate by University of Leeds.

1990   Sale of Thackray's to Corange Ltd; continuation of business under name DePuy International Ltd.

Index